1

The History of Cataclysms

CROSS SECTION OF THE EARTH

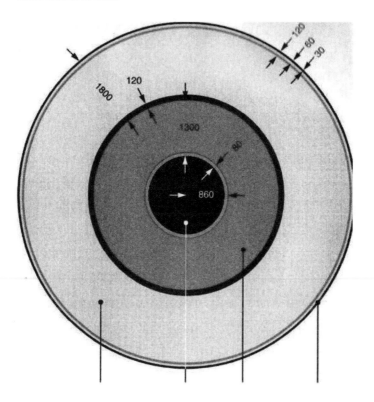

The Adam and Eve Story

By Chan Thomas

Dear Wife

Without her help and faith Through the years of sleepless nights And seemingly endless trails of study, Research, translation, and travel This book Never would have come into being.

General Hal Grant and his wonderful family, to General LeMay and Admiral Taylor, to the Joint Staff of that time, for their inspiring encouragement without which this book might not exist.

To all of those who ridiculed, scorned and laughed relegating me to the nuthouse and even firing me.

For how else would I have been so driven to pursue, solve, find and derive the truth. I owe them.

With a rumble so low as to be inaudible, growing, throbbing, then fuming into a thundering roar, the earthquake starts.....only it's not like any earthquake in recorded history.

In California the mountains shake like ferns in a breeze; the mighty Pacific rears back and piles up into a mountain of seawater more than two miles high.... then starts its race eastward.

With the force of a thousand armies the wind attacks, ripping, shredding everything in its supersonic bombardment. The unbelievable mountain of Pacific seawater follows the wind eastward, burying Los Angeles and San Francisco as if they were but grains of sand.

Nothing - but nothing - stops the relentless, overwhelming onslaught of wind and ocean.

Across the continent the thousand mile-per-hour wind wreaks its hell, its unholy vengeance, everywhere, mercilessly, unceasingly. Every living thing is ripped into shreds while being blown across the countryside; and earthquakes leave no place untouched. In many places the earth's molten sublayer breaks through and spreads a sea of white-hot liquid fire to add to the holocaust.

Within three hours the fantastic wall of seawater moves across the continent, burying the wind-ravaged land under two miles of seething water coast-to-coast.

In a fraction of a day all vestiges of civilization are gone, and the great cities - Los Angeles, San Francisco, Chicago, Dallas, New York, Boston - are nothing but legends. Barely a stone is left where millions walked just a few hours before.

A few lucky ones who manage to find shelter from the screaming wind on the lee side of a high mountain peak - such as Mt. Massive - watch the sea of molten fire breaking through the quaking valleys below. The raging waters follow at supersonic speeds, piling higher and higher, steaming over the molten earth-fire, and rising almost to their feet. Only great, high mountains such as this one can withstand the cataclysmic onslaught.

North America is not alone in her death throes. Central America suffers the same cannonade - wind, earth-fire, and inundation.

South America finds the Andes not high enough to stop the cataclysmic violence pounded out by nature in her berserk rage. In less than a day, Ecuador, Peru, and western Brazil are shaken madly by the devastating earthquake; the Andes are piled higher and higher by the Pacific's supersonic onslaught as it surges over itself against the mountains. The entire continent is burned by molten earth-fire, buried under cubic miles of catastrophically violent seas, then turned into a frozen hell. Everything freezes. Man, beast, plant, and mud are all rock-hard in less than four hours.

Europe cannot escape the onslaught. The raging Atlantic piles higher and higher on itself, following the screeching wind eastward. The

Alps, Pyrenees, Urals, and Scandinavian mountains are shaken, then heaved even higher when the wall of seawater strikes.

Western Africa and the sands of the Sahara vanish in nature's wrath, under savage attack by wind and ocean. The area bounded by Zaire, South Africa, and Kenya suffers only severe earthquakes and winds -little inundation. Survivors there marvel at the Sun, standing still in the sky for nearly half a day.

Eastern Siberia and the Orient suffer a strange fate indeed - as though a giant subterranean scythe sweeps away the earth's foundations, accompanied by the wind in its screaming symphony of supersonic death and destruction. As the Arctic basin leaves its polar home, eastern Siberia, Manchuria, China and Burma are subjected to the same annihilation as South America: wind, earth-fire, inundation, and freezing, jungle animals are shredded to ribbons by the wind, piled into mountains of flesh and bone, and buried under avalanches of homogenized seawater and mud.

Then comes the sudden, seemingly infinite supply of terrible, instantly paralyzing temperature drop of 180 degrees F. Not man, beast, plant, muck, earth, nor water is left unfrozen in the entire eastern Asian continent, most of which remains below sea level.

Antarctica and Greenland, with their ice caps, now rotate around the earth in the Torrid Zone; and the fury of wind and inundation marches on for six days. During the sixth day the oceans start to settle in their new homes, running off the high grounds.

On the seventh day the horrendous rampage is over. The Arctic Ice Age is ended - and a new stone age begins. The oceans - the great homogenizers - have laid down another deep layer of mud over the existing strata in the great plains, as exposed in the Grand Canyon,

Painted Desert, Monument Valley, and the Badlands.

The Bay of Bengal basin, just east of India, is now at the North Pole. The Pacific Ocean, just west of Peru, is at the South Pole. Greenland and Antarctica, now rotating equatorially, find their ice caps dissolving madly in the tropical heat. Massive walls of water and ice surge toward the oceans, taking everything - from mountains to plains - in gushing, heaving paths, while creating immense seasonal moraines. In less than twenty-five years the ice caps are gone, and the oceans around the world rise over two hundred feet with the new-found water. The Torrid Zone will be shrouded in a fog for generations from the enormous amounts of moisture poured into the atmosphere by the melting ice caps.

New ice caps begin to form in the new polar areas.

Greenland and Antarctica emerge with verdant, tropical foliage. Australia is the new, unexplored continent in the North Temperate Zone, with only a few handfuls of survivors populating its vastness. New York lies at the bottom of the Atlantic, shattered, melted by earthfire, and covered by unbelievable amounts of mud. Of San Francisco, Los Angeles, Chicago, Dallas and Boston, not a trace is left. They all will join the legends of the seven cities of Cibola.

What's left of Egypt emerges from its Mediterranean inundation new and higher - still the land of the ages. The commonplace of our time becomes the mysterious Baalbek of the new era.

A new era! Yes, the cataclysm has done its work well. The greatest population regulator of all does once more for man what he refuses to do for himself and the planet on which he lives, and drives the pitiful few who survive into a new stone age.

After this cataclysm we join Noah, Adam and Eve, Atlantis, Mu, and Olympus - and Jesus joins Osiris, Ta'aroa, Zeus, and Vishnu.

THE GREAT FLOODS

Noah? Adam and Eve? Vishnu? Osiris? What do they have in common? They represent eras ages apart and yet, somehow, they all join hands in the next cataclysm, and walk with us.

There are others who walk with us, too: men of science - long forgotten - those who first saw that these tumbles, these cataclysmic catastrophes, or "revolutions" of the earth's shell have happened before, countless times. J. Andre DeLuc in 1779 and Georges Cuvier in 1812 were the foremost. Dolomieu, the famous mineralogist, joined the consensus, as did Escher and Forel, the Swiss geologists; also J. Andre DeLuc Jr. and Von Buch. They all agreed that the cataclysms were caused by sudden revolutions in the wrong direction by the surface of the earth.

Cuvier, in his Theory of the Earth, first published in 1812, based his conclusions on his unparalleled correlative research in stratigraphy, comparative anatomy, and palaeontology. As a matter of fact, Cuvier was (he founder of the science of comparative anatomy, based on his pioneering, self-taught work in that field. At that time he wrote: "Every part of the earth, every hemisphere, every continent, exhibits the same phenomenon.......There has, therefore, been a succession of variations in the economy of organic nature........the various catastrophes which have disturbed the strata........have given rise to numerous shiftings of this (continental) basin. It is of much importance to mark, that these repeated irruptions and retreats of the sea have neither been slow nor gradual; on the contrary, most of the catastrophies which occasioned them have been sudden; and this is especially easy to be proved, with regard to the last of these catastrophes. I agree, therefore, with MM. DeLuc and Dolomieu, in thinking, that if anything in geology be established, it is, that the surface of our globe has undergone a great and sudden revolution, the date of which cannot be. much earlier than five or six thousand years ago....(also), one preceding revolution at least had put (the continents) under water, perhaps two or three irruptions of the sea."

"These alternations now appear to me to form the problem in geology that it is of most importance to solve....in order to solve it satisfactorily, it would be necessary to discover the cause of these events.... These ideas have haunted, 1 may almost say have tormented me, during my researches among fossil bones...... researches which embrace but a very small part of those phenomena of the age preceding the last general revolution of the globe, and which are yet intimately connected with all the others...."

Many attempts have been made to answer the charge made to the geological profession by Cuvier to explain these sudden revolutions in the wrong direction.

Among others, Velikovsky tried it through his studies of myths and legends; Hapgood tried it; Hugh Brown attempted, and in the process amassed a tremendous library of geological data.

Every time the cataclysmic concept has risen, the "beast" has been stoned, burned at the stake, beaten to pulp, and buried with a vengeance; but the corpse won't stay dead. Each time, it raises the lid of its coffin and says in sepulchral tones: "You will die before I."

The latest of the challengers is *Prof. Frank C. Hibben, who in his book, The Lost Americans*,* said: "This was no ordinary extinction of a vague geological period which fizzled to an uncertain end. This death was catastrophic and all inclusive.... What caused the death of forty million animals.... The "corpus delicti" in this mystery may be found almost anywhere.

Their bones lie bleaching in the sands of Florida and in the gravels of New Jersey. They weather out of the dry terraces of Texas and protrude from the sticky ooze of the tar pits off Wilshire Boulevard in Los Angeles.... The bodies of the victims are everywhere....We find literally thousands together....young and old, foal with dam, calf with cow.....The muck pits of Alaska are filled with evidence of universal death....a picture of quick extinction....Any argument as to the cause....must apply to North America, Siberia, and Europe as well.

*Thomas Y. Crowell Co., New York, Apollo Edition, 1961

"....Mammoth and bison were torn and twisted as though by a cosmic hand in a godly rage.

"....In many places the Alaskan muck blanket is packed with animal bones and debris in trainload lots...mammoth, mastodon,....bison, horses, wolves, bears, and lions....A faunal population....in the middle of some cataclysmic catastrophe....was suddenly frozen....in a grim charade."

Supernatural winds; volcanic burning; inundation and burial in muck; preservation by deep-freeze of both torn-up animals and muck. "Any good solution to a consuming mystery must answer all of the facts," challenges Hibben.

The challenge wouldn't leave me alone. Like a hunger, it gnawed at my subconscious. I could hear the deep tones of Cuvier's challenge, "find the cause of these events," still reverberating through the sacred halls of science, ghostly, unanswered. I felt Hibben's challenge, prodding: "....answer all of the facts."

I decided that this cataclysmic concept, this catastrophic end which visits our planet time after time, needed verification or refutation once and for all.

The first step was to gather all of the known, accepted data from as many sciences pertaining to our planet as possible: stratigraphy, archaeology, radiology, anthropology, paleontology, and oceanography, plus cosmology and astronomy - and seismology and oceanography - and paleo-languages such as prehistoric Mayan. Even evolution could not be ignored. Further, cross-correlation of the data between the sciences had to be honored. All of the foregoing gave the answer: although there is enough data in most sciences to indicate that these cataclysms happen, there was not enough in each science to derive the process or prove the concept; but between-science cross correlation showed indeed that the concept was true. Not only did it verify that the events have happened, but disclosed when the last five cataclysms were, and what positions the shell of the Earth has been in for the last 35,000 or more years. This was a first-time effort for certain.

So, after years of research, beginning in 1949, Cuvier's challenge had an answer: Yes, indeed, cataclysms do happen; but I had not yet found the answer to his challenge, find the cause of these events. It would take me twenty more years to find the cause, the trigger of cataclysms. What makes them start? And further, exactly what is it that happens after it starts? What is the process of a cataclysm? Finally, what is the timetable of cataclysms? It was obvious already from the data that it was non-linear. Was it a mathematical function that we could derive from the data? Or is it random and frustrating in its unpredictability? The more learned, the more to be discovered and learned.

Meanwhile, what a chase! And what a dramatic story of the Earth's history we uncovered: Civilizations of more than 20,000 years ago more advanced than our wildest imagination; prehistoric legends from Greece, Egypt, India, and South America which became history instead of legend; lost continents in the Atlantic and Pacific which became dated realities, with logical reasons for their sudden disappearance.

Yes, Vishnu came alive: a man who lived through a cataclysm many thousands of years ago - actually ten cataclysms ago! Now he is known as the Hindu god of ten resurrections from the waters. Osiris was rediscovered; he was the Jesus of his time - a man of Egypt, some 15,000 years ago. Noah smiled at us from the pages of The Epic of Gilgamesh; he actually was a Sumerian named Utnapishtim, who lived just around 7,000 years ago. The ark he built is more than legend.

The process of a cataclysm is known now.

Look at the cross-section of the Earth inside the front cover. You'll see two molten layers - the yellow ones. The important one is the thin molten layer starting 60 miles down, extending 60 miles deeper to 120 miles below the surface of the Earth. The thick, deep molten layer, starting 1,800 miles down at the bottom of the mantle, and extending 1,300 miles deeper, is the outer core. Seismology has proven these two yellow layers to be molten, and they arc white-hot. Over 2500 degrees Fahrenheit.

The outer, 60-mile thick layer is the one which supplies the volcanoes with the molten lava they spew forth.

Inside the Earth, the electrical and magnetic structure of the interior makes these layers act as if they were near solid, or plastic. As long as the interior magnetic and electrical structure of the Earth maintains its orderliness, this old Earth keeps on rotating on its axis in a normal manner.

If anyone doubts that Antarctica's ice cap is growing, it has been proven that it is growing at the rate of a Lake Ontario per year. So is Greenland growing. Since they are not centered on the Earth's axis of rotation, they develop centrifugal forces coupling with each other, in a direction perpendicular to the Earth's axis. It's like swinging a bucket of water around yourself on a rope. The water stays in the bucket; if you did not have the restraining rope, the bucket and water would fly away. In the case of the ice caps, the restraining rope is gravity, which keeps these two ice caps landlocked. Since these ice caps therefore cannot fly away, they resolve their problem by trying to pull the entire shell of the Earth above the 60-mile thick molten layer around the interior of the Earth. As long as the electrical and magnetic structure is maintained inside the Earth, the ice caps cannot pull the shell around to let them to go to the equator, and we maintain our orderly, daily, monthly, yearly rotation.

Right now we don't known why, every few thousand years on a varying timetable, the magnetic and electrical orderliness in the shallow molten layer is disorganized. Further, it is not known by what means it is disrupted. It has to be a way which lowers those energies to the extent that the shallow molten layer is allowed to act as a free liquid, letting the molten layer act as a molten liquid which then serves as a lubricant for the ice caps to pull the shell around the Earth's interior so as to have the ice caps shift about 90 degrees into the Torrid Zone.

In one quarter to one half a day, the geographic poles move to the Torrid Zone, and all hell lets loose. The atmosphere and the Earth's oceans and lakes don't shift with the shell - they just keep on rotating west to east - and at the equator that speed is about 1,037 miles per hour. It has to be, normally, to make one revolution per day. So, while the shell shifts with the poles going to the equator, the winds and oceans continue eastward, blowing and flooding across the earth at supersonic speeds, inundating continents with water miles deep, destroying everything with which man ever dealt, including himself. That's a summary of the process.

Now what about the trigger? This turned out to be the most elusive piece of the whole puzzle. We couldn't rely on some supernatural assumption - like sometime happenings in the heavens of a vague character which actually violated the laws of nature; no, it had to be something natural, a part of nature's ordinary structure, which disrupts the Earth's inner electrical and magnetic structure whenever a cataclysm happens. It also has to be a kind of happening which decreases the inner electrical and magnetic forces to the extent that they cannot support keeping the shallow molten layer acting as if it were plastic, or near solid.

We once thought that severe Sun spots could be the cause, because they do disrupt the Earth's inner electrical and magnetic structure, but we were wrong.

The time wasted on that assumption was the price for dealing in assumptions rather than facts. It was a bad detour to take. What was necessary was to be patient, to take more time; to assemble more facts; and use our most valuable tool, analytical reasoning. The solution, whatever it might be, would come.

The derivation of the process gave us a greater understanding of prehistoric events. For instance, you can see that ice ages are not a matter of advancing and retreating ice; it's simply that different areas of the Earth are in polar regions at different times, for different durations of time; changes between positions take place in a fraction of a day, and the accompanying supersonic deluges deposit the various huge stratas we find in the walls of the Grand Canyon, Painted Desert, Monument Valley, the mountains around Mexican Hat, Canyon de Chelly, and the Moqui Dugway.

The story around the world gives silent testimony:

- The Beresovka mammoth, frozen in mud, with buttercups in his mouth;

- The age of the gorges below Niagara Falls and St. Anthony's Falls, both about 7,000 years;

- The sudden end of the Laurentian Basin ice cap in Canada, about 1 1,500 years ago;

- The uninterrupted evolution on the Galapagos, over 11,000 years;

- The geological datings in the Murrumbidgee River basin system in Australia, showing the end of an ice cap there about 11,500 years ago;

- The age of fossil bones taken from the Wilshire Boulevard tar pits, over 11,000 years;

- The sudden end of all work in the prehistoric city of Tiahuanaco, Bolivia, 11,500 years ago;

- Leonard Woolley's great work in the Holy Land, dating Noah's flood at about 6,000 years ago;

- The end of the Wisconsin ice cap, about 29,000 years ago;

- The sudden 200-foot rise of the oceans all over the world, about 7,000 years ago;

- The sudden rise of the St. Lawrence River bed <100 years ago;

- The changing levels of the shoreline of the Hudson On i n (Canada;

- The huge granite blocks from the Alps, sitting on iIh eastern slopes of the Jura mountains at 4,000 feet above sea level;

- The great legendarian Fraser's uncovering of over Il 00(1 verified separate inundation survival legends in die Malay Peninsula region;

- The Pejark Marsh in Australia, which shows a quick extinction of many, many species, including humans, 11,500 years ago;

- The Piri Reis map, showing the North Pole in Egypt;

- The Egyptian water-clock, showing agreement with the Piri Reis map;

- Granite on top of the mountains around Death Valley in California;

- The great stratifications of the Grand Canyon, Painted Desert, Monument Valley, and Badlands, each layer homogenous, showing it to be deposited there suddenly by fantastic amounts of superswift water;

- The present growth of the Antarctic ice cap, approximately 293 cubic miles of ice per year;

The legends from primitive man in Tierra del Fuego at the southern tip of South America of the day the Sun set in the wrong direction;

- The legends from primitive man in Peru of the day the Sun stood still;

- The legends from Malayan and Sumatran tribal aborigines of the long night;

- The varve (earth strata) counts in Wrenshall, Minnesota, and Hackensack, New Jersey, which conform with each other;

- The prevalence of jade in the Orient, which is material heaved up from the mantle, near equatorial pivot points during a cataclysm;

- The fantastic evidence of burgeoning tropical plants in Arctic Siberia, Alaska and Antarctica, frozen and preserved for thousands of years in a fraction of a day during a cataclysm;

- The similarity of languages the world over, from Polynesian to Greek, to Egyptian, to Mayan, to Eskimo, to Yakut, to Oriental, and more;

- The footprints of dinosaurs, imprinted in beds of exposed river mud, frozen before the prints could deteriorate, remaining frozen for thousands of years to allow the mud prints to ossify for us to see as dinosaur footprints in rock beds today;

- The correlation of ice ages, stone ages, and quick extinctions of all species the world over;

- The survival of primitive life at the equatorial pivot points - the last two being the Malay Peninsula and the Galapagos, both now rife with lizards;

- The existence of a coral reef on the floor of the Arctic Ocean;

- And more, and more, and more, and more, give us a prehistoric picture of the positions of the Earth's shell during the past 35,000 or more years;

- The overwhelming evidence, when put in order, gives a dramatic picture of which areas have been at the North Pole, when they moved to the pole, when they moved away from the pole, and how long they were there. The chart is on the next page.

Notice that the end of an era is the same as the start of the next era. Although the chart is in terms of years ago and years duration, do remember that the change from one era to the next occurs in a fraction of a day - short enough to be called abrupt.

Areas at North Pole (North Polar Eras)	Start	End	Duration (Years)
	(Years Ago)		
Arctic Ocean	7,000	?	?
Sudan Basin	11,500	7,000	4,500
Hudson Bay	18,500	11,500	7,000
Caspian Sea	29,000	18,500	10,500
Wisconsin	?	29,000	?

Yes, Noah, Adam and Eve, Osiris, Ta'aroa, Zeus, and Vishnu have much deeper meaning now; and, as they join hands and walk with us, we hear Adam and Eve saying:

"Listen - for now we can truly share our story with you!"

THE STORY

Enigma..

Pursuit..

Unraveling..

It's funny how some things can plague you from your childhood years through your adult years. Not big things, necessarily, but little things, which don't exactly persistm but annoyingly stick their heads through your life's door and say "Boo!" just to let you know they're still there. If I made a list of all these things in my life it might take up a whole book.

I'd like to talk about just one of these bugaboos. From the first time I heard the story of the creation and Adam and Eve, even as a child it bothered me. To me, the answer wasn't simply one of two usual alternatives: either unquestioning faith in the story as it stands, or complete repudiation as utter nonsense.

No, the answer seemed to lie elsewhere. If the story were taught as the truth so uniformly, in spite of its apparent divergence from scientific truths, then to me the true course would seem to be a search for the foundation of the story, which would then lead to a true reading of it.

The pursuit happened almost by accident. Years of data correlation in studying cataclysmology has shown the last cataclysm to have occurred about 7,000 years ago; that Noah, or Utnapishtim, or whatever his name was, did exist and did survive that cataclysm.

A friend of mine suggested that Genesis I is almost a perfect description of conditions on our planet right after a cataclysm, including about a week following. On rereading it, I had to agree; Genesis II even mentions that a mist (proper translation: inundation) arose from the earth and watered the whole face of the ground.

Well, now! This was worth thinking about. If it were so, then it would be the cataclysm preceding Noah's (another fascinating story!), about 11,500 years ago. This, then, could be approximately the time of the Adam and Eve Story.

The pursuit started. If the story did originate with that cataclysm, in what language was it first written? Certainly not Hebrew or Greek, for as far as we know, they didn't even exist at that time. Was it possible to delve into the vanished pages of prehistory and find both the language and the story as originally written?

If we look to men such as Don Antonio Batres Jaurequi and James Churchward, we may have our answer. Certainly their knowledge of prehistoric languages could be a key, and later we'll discuss the role of Naga and ancient Mayan in the story of Adam and Eve; first, however, let's examine the history of Genesis I, II and III.

There are many schools of thought on this subject; the predominant one is that Moses was the originator.

This seems not obtuse, since Moses was reared in the Egyptian tradition, in a royal household; he probably had access to many religious writings and teachings now lost with the passing of the archives in Egypt, in Alexandria, Heliopolis, and Sais. Certainly the Ten Commandments were a condensation of the forty-two questions of Osiris for entering heaven. If Moses did write part of the Old Testament, he then must have had Naga table writings, or Egyptian interpretations of them, handed down to the Egyptians for thousands of years through the royal households; and the Egyptian priesthood had knowledge of a cataclysm 11,500 years ago (from our time). Priests of Egypt are supposed to have told Solon during his ten years in Egypt (about 600 B.C) that 9,000 years before that time there was cataclysm which buried Atlantis beneath the ocean. Note that 9,000 + 600 B.C. + 1,950 A.D. = 11,550 years ago.

Moses' brother, Aaron, became the first chief priest of the Hebrews about 1,300 B.C. Somewhere between 15 and 18 generations later, the chief priesthood having been handed down from father to son through the generations, Seraiah (or Seraias) was the chief priest (See Ezra, and 1 & 2 Ezdras). Later, in 586 B.C., in the 19th year of Nebuchadnezzar's reign, Seraiah was executed, and his son Ezra made a captive in Persia (See 2 Kings). Jerusalem was sacked, and all Hebrew laws and records of the Old Testament were burned with the temple at Jerusalem, by Nebuza-adan, Nebuchadnezzar's Captain of the Guard.

In 458 B.C., the seventh year of Artaxerxes' reign in Persia, Ezra was commissioned to reestablish the Hebrew religion and law. According to 2 Ezdras, Ezdra rewrote the history of the Hebrews from the beginning, and reestablished their laws.

Now, from 586 to 458 B.C. is 128 years. The latest that Ezra could have been born was after his father Seraiah's execution, as well could be (see Onan's story, Genesis 38:8 through 10); therefore, the youngest he could have been in 458 B.C. was 127. He was working on a long memory.

Let's examine this anomaly. As mentioned before, the lineage from Aaron to Ezra contains from 17 to 20 generations, including Aaron and Ezra. Assuming (1) 1,300 B.C. to be the start of Aaron's priesthood (1,290 B.C. is adjudged to be the time of the Exodus); (2) 458 B.C. to be near the end of Ezra's priesthood; then we find the average priesthood term per generation to be between 42.1 and 49.5 years. In view of this, can we believe that Ezra served his priesthood for approximately 130 years? Which includes his entire life span?

It would appear much more plausible to assume that it was Ezra's grandfather Azariah, rather than his father Seraiah, who was the one taken

39

and executed by Nebuchadnezzar's men in 586 B.C. Then Seraiah and Ezra would have served as chief priests from 586 to 458 B.C., for an average of 64 years apiece. It is even plausible Ezra's great-grandfather Helchiah could have been the victim in 586 B.C., leaving Azariah, Seraiah Ezra to serve the 128 years for an average of 42 years each, which is even closer to the overall average of 42.1 to 49.5 years from Aaron to Ezra, over a period of about 845 years.

This means that the Adam and Eve story was last seen in writing by Helchiah or Azariah, therefore handed down verbally possibly by Azariah, and certainly by Seraiah and Ezra, and finally dictated by Ezra to five scribes. It is the five scribes' writings that we have today as Ezra's work. And the English is not even a literal translation... for instance, "without form and void" more literally would read "raging inundations and horrendous winds"...

Now, through Ezra's reconstruction of Genesis, we are told many things:

1- Because of the use of tree, fruit, serpent, cherubim, word of fire, and other words of Moses which were glyphs in the picture language of prehistory, it is evident that the Creation and Adam and Eve stories were probably written in the glyphs of Naga, the predominant Eastern hemisphere language of 11,500 years ago. This language is nearly identical to Prehistoric Mayan, and the progenitor of many languages, which include Oriental and Polynesian tongues, Egyptian, Greek and Yakut. My own knowledge of prehistoric Naga and Mayan glyphs enable me to read many Indian blankets of the Southwestern United States, which have woven into them colorful glyphs depicting a cataclysm. I wonder if the Indians are chuckling to themselves, knowing that the tourists think they are buying blankets of just pretty pictures.

Yakut is an interesting language. It is almost pure spoken Naga. It is spoken by Alaskan Eskimos; the town of Yakutat means "The place where Yakut is spoken". It is also spoken by a native tribe in Turkey. Naga in almost its purest prehistoric form is spoken by a tribe in northern India. It is pure prehistoric Mayan.

2- Moses certainly, and possibly Aaron, had access to the royal Egyptian glyph-stones library.

3- Neither Moses nor Aaron knew how to read the ancient glyph languages of Naga or Mayan, therefore read the glyphs quite literally.

4- Not being able to read the symbolism of the glyphs, in addition to reading them literally, Moses and Aaron (and possibly Ezra) read into the Adam and Eve story the social and religious attitudes of their day. In that time woman was regarded as the root of all sin, a lowly creature, her birth recorded only as an exception, and basically being the cause of man's every downfall - a daily potential. This attitude persists even in worse forms in some religions amazingly in our time.

Is it any wonder that Eve was shouldered with the responsibility for the downfall of all mankind, as a trend of interpretations read into the Naga by Moses? And into Moses' reading by Ezra? Perhaps also it was read into the story by Egyptian priests long before Moses' time, and passed on to him verbally as history. If his father were really the one taken and executed by the Captain of the Guard, Nebuza-adan, then it had to be his grandfather who passed the story to him verbally.

The fusing of two stories (P and J versions) into one to make the story of Genesis I, II, and III may confuse "the man" with Adam. It is possible that Adam, being only nine generations ahead of Noah, with the time span of the Sudan Basin Polar Era covering about 4,500 to 5,000 years, was not "the man" referred to in the creation, but his name and experiences were merged with "the man's" story.

Remember, however, we are informed that Ezra dictated the entire history to five scribes from memory, and this work contains Genesis as we know it today. For him to recall from the archives of his mind what he did well as he did - certainly bespeaks of inspiration of a high order; but it also appears evident that he had no knowledge of the fact that 4,500 years transpired between Genesis I and Noah's flood. It is clear from 2 Ezdras 3:9 that Genesis I and Noah's flood were actually two inundations, however, for while speaking of the two occasions, he says of Noah's flood: "And again in process of time thou broughtest the flood upon those that dwelt in the world, and destroyedst them."

Now, we mentioned before that the lineage of the high priests from Aaron to Ezra differs in numbers of generations (17 or 20) and names as presented in 1 and 2 Ezdras; and both differ in names from the book of Ezra. We also find differences in the lineages from Noah to Jesus (approximately 51 generations) in the Bible. Is it any wonder, therefore, that some generations could have been omitted in the Adam to Noah line? Not to mention the Noah to Jesus line? And the Aaron to Ezra line?

And in light of the fact that, in addition to overwhelming evidence, there are countless legends in the Asia-Pacific areas, handed down from the inundation of 11,500 years ago, of a creation much like that of Genesis I and II, is it not possible that "the man" of the Genesis story became confused with Adam throughout the thousands of years, and through a succeeding cataclysm in Noah's time 7,000 years ago?

The miracle is that the whole story of "creation " and of Adam and Eve is as undistorted as it is; being 11,500 years old, it has suffered through many debacles visited upon its guardians in the intervening years.

Because of the lack of resolving information, "the man" and Adam are kept as one in this translation-interpretation.

5- The significant Naga glyphs given to us by Ezra through Moses' direct reading are: Cherubims, Rib, Adam's sleep, Man, Woman, Tree, Fruit on the tree, Serpent, and Flaming Sword.

Our knowledge of Naga glyphs tells us that the tree (of life) symbolized a mother continent, a parent civilization lasting thousands of years longer than ours of today.

An unadorned serpent represented water in its natural state, or the ocean; a serpent entwined around the tree signified that the mother continent was surrounded entirely by water. Genesis III, 15 actually describes Eve's heel on the serpent's head, depicting her victory over the oceans.

Cherubims - which were not pretty, plump babies as we have always thought - but glyphs of hybrid man and beast. They were the glyphs for legs, or foundations, or underpinnings. Instead of being placed in the garden of Eden, the foundation was taken away, and a Naga or Mayan reading of the Egyptian Book of the Dead shows that cherubims of the North, South, East and West were taken away -meaning that all the foundations of the mother continent were removed and destroyed.

The flaming sword was the symbol of fire and earthquake. The fire signified what all legends of these cataclysms call earth-fire, which is the planet-wide molten layer below the Earth's 60-mile thick shell breaking through to the surface during a cataclysm, a literal hell. It is, as far as I have been able to determine, the origin of man's concept of hell.

I remember watching John Kennedy's funeral on television; and most vividly the incantation given by the Archbishop to keep John Kennedy from the doors of hell. His words went back to pre-Christian Rome, for in describing those gates of hell, he painted a picture of hell exactly like that of the molten sublayer breaking through the earth's shell. It had to be handed down through thousands of years from one who had actually seen it. Chills ran up and down my spine as it stamped an indelible impression on my mind.

Now to the tree: Fruit growing on that tree symbolized the mankind which settled the mother continent ages before Adam and Eve. Their eating the fruit tells us they were descended from this original mankind. Eve eating first signifies that she was the younger generation; Adam eating second signifies that he was her father, which made her his daughter. His daughter!? Yes. It is the origin of one of the oldest Hebrew laws: In a catastrophe, if but a male and female survive, they must mate, regardless of their relationship.

If you want to check on this, read the story of Lot and his two daughters. The daughters were simply obeying Hebrew law. He is stated to be too drunk to know what he was doing. Ha! If he were, he couldn't have performed. He must have been a good actor.

The glyph of the creation is even more revealing. There are three figures represented on the stone; the top figure is the face of a sleeping or dead person (there were no separate symbols for death and sleep in Naga - both were represented as the same). The middle figure is shown as a male, and the bottom figure a female who is represented as the mother of all mankind. In addition, there are curved lines from the sleeping or dead person and the male middle figure to the bottom of the female figure.

This glyph has been interpreted to mean that the middle figure, a male, was put to sleep, shown by the top figure, and a rib (or ribs) removed from him (the ribs being the curved lines) and

49

fashioned into the bottom figure, the female mother of all mankind. This fits beautifully with the story of Eve's creation, Adam therefore being both the male middle figure and the top figure, a sleeping or dead person.

There is a hitch to this story, however: the top figure, either sleeping or dead, is depicted as a female! How could it be Adam, asleep, awake, dead or alive?

Moreover, in Naga the curved lines denote parentage rather than ribs; so, more reasonably, it appears that the top figure is a dead female, whose offspring by the male middle figure (Adam) was the bottom female figure (Eve), the mother of all mankind.

I have been asked countless times how one can tell the top figure to be a dead female, to the extent that I guess I owe an answer here.

In Naga and prehistoric Mayan, they show that they worshipped but one Deity, and represented that Deity by a glyph of a circle representing the Sun. Any time a circle was shown on a tablet, it could only represent their Deity.

This tablet has two circles on it. "Purists" have stated that the "writers" of this tablet meant to show "double intensity" of the Deity. Strange; I have never seen anywhere a "double intensity" of two circles in either Naga or prehistoric Mayan. The curious thing about these two circles is that they are located precisely where a female's breasts should be on the top figure. Maybe that's what "double intensity" is all about!

The most curious thing about this stone is that it fits the legend of Adam being a widower, and the name of his deceased wife being Lilith. If true, it would also reveal Lilith to be Eve's mother.

So, in essence, the story as read from the glyphs would be that Adam and Eve, who lived in the Garden of Eden on the mother continent (tree), were descended from the original mankind (fruit) of that land, which incidentally was surrounded entirely by water (serpent entwined around the tree). Eve was Adam's daughter, and he was a widower.

They realized that, in order to survive, they had to leave and never try to return, for the motherland was destined to be destroyed by a cataclysmic inundation. Eve had perceived this coming event, and Adam asked her how she had discovered it; she answered that she had inherited the intelligence to do so from her ancestors. As a result she had gained victory over the inundation (Eve's heel on the serpent's head).

They left the motherland; and afterward the continent (tree) was subjected to a fiery earthquake (flaming sword), during which it lost its foundations (cherubims) and sank beneath the ocean (serpent) which remained forever afterward burying the continent (forever afterward crawling on its belly).

So let's review the event - two cataclysms ago - and then apply our knowledge toward a representative translation-interpretation of Genesis I, II, and III. It may be the most accurate reading of a story written 11,500 years ago.

THE EVENT

11,500 Years Ago

Did you ever sit down for an evening at a card table with a 1,000-piece puzzle? By yourself? It takes hours and hours to put it together, doesn't it, with trial and error - and patience - all playing their parts.

We're still trying out some of the as yet unfitted pieces in our worldwide puzzle, and we've been "at the table" since 1949. However, even though still not complete, it shows us a graphic representation of the Earth's picture as it was 11,500 years ago.

Look at a globe of the World. Pick out Longitude 90 degrees W -Latitude 60 degrees N. This point is in the western part of the Hudson Bay.

Now hold the globe so that the spot 90 deg. W - 60 deg. N is at the North Pole, on the axis of rotation. This was the configuration of the World between 18,500 years ago and 11,500 years ago. The North Polar ice cap formed the Laurentian Basin in Canada.

The continents, however, were not quite the same. There was a huge continent in the Atlantic Ocean, which stretched from England across the Atlantic to the Bahamas. The Caribbean Sea and possibly even the Gulf of Mexico did not exist; there is evidence of the Caribbean being land at that time. An ice cap on the globe's opposite side from Hudson Bay covered western Australia, and eastern Australia was burgeoning with humans, animals, birds, vegetation, and rivers.

There was another continent in the pacific covering an area now ringed by the Hawaiian Islands, the Galapagos, Easter Island, Tahiti, the Solomons, and the Caroline Islands. Have you ever noticed the heavy sedimentary stratifications making up the top half of Diamond Head? They have the same characteristics of the strata exposed in the walls of Grand Canyon, Monument Valley and the mysterious Canyon de Chelly.

The Province of Ceylon held the major civilization of India. Ahoydia in northern India was the thriving capital of that country. It was then called Adjudia.

Greece - land of the Hellenes - was the home of a tall, blue-eyed, blonde race with standards of science and law unmatched to this day.

The Amazon basin was an inland sea - legends call it the Sea of Xarayes - and the mouth of the Amazon River was then a wide, seagoing connection between the Atlantic and the Sea of Xarayes. The western coast of South America was not mountainous -indications are that the prehistoric city of Tiahuanaco, Bolivia, now at 12,500 feet above sea level, was at sea level. It was a metropolis seaport, with a canal system for seagoing ships - as large as any today - traversing from the Pacific to an inland sea. If you wish to read details about this, read The Calendar of Tiahuanaco and

The Great Idol of Tiahuanaco, both by Hans Schindler Bellamy and Peter Allan. They make terrific reading.

Astronomers of Tiahuanaco used telescopes like ours of today; and they had a huge satellite orbiting the Earth - West to East, 449 times per year - which they used as a time standard, its orbit was so accurate.

Ahoydia, now a suburb of Lucknow, was the capital of India. And the great navigators, the great scientists, the great explorers of the eastern hemisphere were the dark-eyed, dark-haired Mayans. India had gravity-propelled vehicles and gravity-made weaponry.

About 11,500 years ago - in 9,550 B.C., as dated by astronomers from Potsdam Observatory from writings in the ruins of Tiahuanaco, the 60-mile thick shell of the Earth shifted its position once more in 1/4 to 1/2 a day, about 7,000 years after the previous shift. The North Pole moved southward, and the Sudan Basin in Africa shifted to the North Pole. This was the time, as the Talmud states, when the setting of the Pleiades below the horizon occurred and "The Holy Land was moved into a region of terrible cold" for many generations, actually for about 4,500 to 5,000 years until Noah's flood, about 7,000 years ago.

The equatorial pivot points were off the coast of mid-Chile and in mid-China, near the Yangtze, north of Vietnam.

The great continent in the Pacific disappeared almost completely -what is now Easter Island, then on the edge of the continent, dropped to remain on the Pacific Ocean floor for about 5,000 years -to be heaved up in the cataclysm causing Noah's flood. What remained of the vast Pacific continent rolled to the South Pole, to be discovered by Mayan explorers as the last remains of their motherlands - a "frozen reservoir of mud at the bottom of the Earth," millions of square miles in area. Today we see indications of the continent in the sedimentary strata in the heights of Diamond Head in the Hawaiians, and the same stratifications in most of the higher Pacific islands.

Of the great continent in the Atlantic, only a large island was left in the West, while the ocean between there and Gibraltar to the East was left shallow, muddy, and impassable to ships.

A thread of a clue concerning the great knowledge of that time came out when Captain Cook discovered the Polynesian Maori tribe in New Zealand in the 1700's. They told him of ancient legends of Saturn's rings - and they hadn't even heard of telescopes. Now you try to see those rings with your naked eyes - and you'll find out that it's impossible.

The evidence in Tiahuanaco shows that their great civilization was wiped out so suddenly that people were caught in the middle of their normal daytime activities by a catastrophic inundation. Further, evidence shows that this fabulous city suffered the same fate as Easter Island: although the Rockies and Andes were started in this cataclysm, Tiahuanaco was buried under the Pacific, to remain there for almost 5,000 years, then to be heaved up to its present altitude of 12,500 feet in the last cataclysm about 7,000 years ago.

So the cataclysm of 11,500 years ago saw the Hudson Bay and the opposite area just southwest of Australia both roll to the equator on opposite sides of the Earth, and the Sudan basin roll to the North Pole, to remain there for about the next 4,500 to 5,000 years. While this shift was occurring, taking only 1/4 to 1/2 a day to complete itself, the Earth's oceans and atmosphere, through angular momentum, kept rotating in their normal direction during most of the shift, with the oceans violently inundating most of the lands of the Earth at supersonic speeds, and the atmosphere bringing unimaginable hurricanes of supersonic wind velocities. Whole continents were subjected to tremendous upheavals and earthquakes. Huge mountain ranges were created. The 60-mile thick molten layer below the 60-mile thick shell of the Earth broke through the shell in places all over the world, and was thereafter called "Earth-fire" by the pitiful few who survived.

Pitiful Few? The whole Earth? Best estimates are less than one percent of all life on our Earth.

The oceans and winds took six days after the start of the cataclysm to resolve their holocaustic wars on the surface of the Earth, and on the seventh day began to settle down to about 5,000 years of normal activity and complacency. The two-mile thick ice caps of the Laurentian Basin and the Indian Ocean, having shifted from their polar homes and started a new course of revolving equatorially, proceeded to melt at tremendous speeds in the torrid heat, carving great grooves in the mountains as the rushing, gushing, swirling water and ice overwhelmed everything in their paths. The great amounts of moisture being poured into the atmosphere were to shroud the Torrid Zone in a dark fog for many years during several generations. The oceans rose some 200 to 300 feet all over the world with the sudden melting of the ice caps as they do after each cataclysm.

The end of the Laurentian Ice Age and the start of the "old stone age" was complete.

The Mayan tongue lived on in scattered remnants: Polynesian tongues, Greek, Yakut, Egyptian, Eskimo tongues, Nomadic, Oriental, German, American Indian - just about all languages. The resurrection from the waters - Tau - lived on in many stories from the Pacific of a man who survived, later to become Ta'aroa, Tongaroa, or Taroa'a, depending on which tribe's legend you find. Adam and Eve could have sprung from the same story. Who knows?

GENESIS: 4,500,000,000 YEARS AGO, THIS REGENESIS: 11,500 YEARS AGO, Both in the Bible

A translation-interpretation of Genesis I, II, and III, from a reconstruction of what the Naga must have been to give us the chapters as we have them in English; then retranslating directly from Naga to English, bypassing Greek and Hebrew.

THE BOOK of GENESIS (Chapters I, II, and III)

I.

1. In the beginning (4.32 billion years ago) the universe was created in God's great design. Included was our Sun, and our planet Earth.

2. And during one of the many cataclysms that occurred during the earth's history (this one being 11,500 years ago), the earth's lands were all inundated with raging waters, and ravaged by horrendous winds; and the oceans were all dark with

muddiness. And the ill wind thundered over the troubled waters also.

3. And as the storms abated, sunlight came back to the face of the earth, as God intended.

4. And, while the cataclysm was abating, once more darkness and sunlight were reestablished and distinguishable, and it was good.

5. And sunlight was again daytime, and darkness again nighttime, in accordance with God's design; and evening and morning made one day.

6. Again, God's original design was that there be a sky between the clouds and oceans;

7. And in accordance with God's design, the heavens were reestablished, in that the sky again stood between the clouds and the oceans, as the onslaught of the great cataclysm abated.

8. And God's heavens were indeed reestablished; and that evening and morning were the beginning of the second day.

9. And God's design was that the lands would not be entirely covered by the oceans as they were immediately following a cataclysm, so the disrupted oceans, now settling, drained off the higher lands.

10. And, in accordance with God's design, the dry land was earth, and the waters oceans, and once again it was reestablished and good, as God intended.

11. And since God's design was that the earth should bring forth grass and herbs, yielding their seed, and the fruit yielding fruit containing its seed; and the earth was again reestablished.

12. Therefore the earth, being reestablished, brought forth grass and herbs, yielding their seed, and the fruit tree yielding fruit containing its seed; and it was good, as God intended.

13. And the evening and the morning were the start of the third day.

14. In accordance with God's design, there were normally lights in the heavens, which served to indicate months, and seasons, and days, and years;

15. Also they served to furnish light on the earth, as God intended.

16. And as the great fog lifted, and the clouds broke, the Sun and the Moon reappeared, and also the stars;

17. And once again, as God intended, they shone from the heavens;

18. And the Sun and the Moon again were able to divide light and darkness, which was good.

19. And the evening and the morning were the start of the fourth day.

20. And it was God's will that some of every creature living, and bird flying, should survive the cataclysmic Inundation.

21. Surviving then were the great whales, and every living, creature of the sea, and every kind of winged fowl/ and it was as God intended, and good.

22. And they were blessed with God's original design to be fruitful, and reproduce, and replenish the oceans with sea life and the air with fowl.

23. And the evening and the morning were the start of the fifth day.

24. And it was God's will that some of every creature, cattle, and creeping thing, and beast of the earth, should survive the

cataclysmic inundation;

25. Surviving then were the beasts, the cattle, and every thing that creeps on the earth; and it was as God intended, and good.

26. And in accordance with God's design, man, who was created in the image God intended, also was to survive, and have dominion over the fowl of the air, and over the cattle, and over the earth, and over every creeping thing that creeps on the earth.

27. So it was God's design that man, who was created in the image God intended, both male and female, would survive the cataclysmic inundation.

28. And they were blessed with God's original design to be fruitful, and multiply, and replenish the earth, and control it; and have dominion over the fish of the sea, and over the fowl of the air, and over every living thing that moves on the earth.

29. And God's design was that man, being given every herb bearing seed, which is upon the face of all the earth, and every tree, in which is the fruit of a tree yielding seed; to man it should be for food.

30. And to every beast of the earth, and to every fowl of the air, and to every thing that creeps on the earth, wherein there is life, God's design was that green herbs shall serve for food; and it was as God intended.

31. And every thing which survived, was as God had originally created, and still was in God's design, and was good. And the evening and the morning were the beginning of the sixth day.

II.

1. Thus the heavens and the earth were reestablished, all the host of them.

2. And on the seventh day the recovery from the cataclysm and flood were complete; and the

seventh day brought rest from the fight for survival against the cataclysm and its aftereffects.

3. And the seventh day brought God's blessed peace, as the cataclysm had abated, leaving those of his creation who survived.

4. These are the same regenerations of the heavens and of the earth as they were reestablished after the cataclysm previous to the one of this story, when the Lord God reestablished the earth and the heavens.

5. And every plant of the field before that cataclysm was in the earth, and every herb in the field before it grew. For the Lord God had not brought rain upon the earth in this region, and there was not a man to till the ground.

6. But there was this cataclysm, and great inundations rose over the earth.

7. And it was God's will that man should rise up from the earth, and keep the breath of life, and remain a living soul. This is his story.

8. And it was God's will, after a cataclysm, that a continent eastward be established, and there in Eden lived the man of this story.

9. And from this land grew other civilizations, on other lands, with the motherland in the midst of all being the seat of wisdom, of all knowledge, both good and evil.

10. And the inundation destroyed Eden, and left only its four offspring lands.

(Note: The next four verses are probably incorrect or incomplete, with the true descriptions locked in correct translations of Egypt's Book of the Dead, and the missing portion of the Piri Reis map.)

11. The first land is near the river Pison, which includes the whole land of Havilah, where there is gold;

12. And the gold of that land is good: there is bdellium and the onyx stone.

13. And the second land is near the river Gihon: the same land which includes the whole land of Ethiopia.

14. And the third land is near the river Hiddekel: that is the land toward the east of Assyria. And the fourth land is near the river Euphrates.

I5. And it was in God's province that the man was of Eden, where he lived and toiled.

I6. And he was descended from the original mankind which settled that motherland.

17. And God's design was that the man was warned: although the motherland was the source of all knowledge, both good and evil, that if he stay therein, surely he would die.

18. And it was God's design that the man should not be alone, therefore a mate should be his;

19. And since God had originally created every beast of the field, and fowl of the air, and in his time Adam had named each one;

20. And Adam gave names to all cattle, and to the fowl of the air, and to every beast of the field; but for Adam there was no mate.

21. For Adam's mate had died, after giving birth to a child of Adam;

22. And the child of the man was a female, made in the image God intended;

23. And Adam said, this child is bone of my bone, and flesh of my flesh; and she grew into womanhood.

24. Therefore, the man was both father and mother to her, and she abode with him, and they were one flesh.

25. And the climate there was warm, requiring little or no clothing.

III.

1. Now at the time of the beginning of this story, the oceans were in their normal state of quietness; and it was known to the woman of this story that she was not descended from any of the peoples of the lands which sprang from the mother continent;

2. And God's design was that the woman would learn that people of the offspring lands would live on,

3. But the people of the motherland, from whom she had descended, would surely all die.

4, And she knew that in spite of the impending inundation, she surely would not die;

5. For God's design was that from the day she was born, she was descended from the original mankind of the motherland,

and was destined to know all, to discern both good and evil.

6. And the woman, being of the motherland, and being wise and good, knew that both she and her father were descended from the original mankind of the motherland.

7. And they both were wise, and had lived the good life; and it was that time of the year when some clothing was needed for warmth.

8. And in the cool of those days, when they were wondering to which of the offspring lands they should go, and God's presence was felt strongly by them,

9. Adam feltGod's call, 10. And said, I have heard God warning since summer, and have feared, for I knew not where to find refuge;

11. And God's warning had come to him in the summer, as a warning to leave the land of his ancestors.

1 2. And the man said, the woman who is my daughter, and descended from my ancestors, gave me this knowledge;

13. And asked her, What gift of knowledge has God given you? And the woman said, I am of your ancestors and inherit their wisdom; and the coming inundations of the oceans has been made known to me;

14. And God's design was that the oceans would so inundate the lands, and drown all cattle, and all beasts of the field, and bury all dust,

15. And God has thus given me victory over the oceans, such that the seed of future generations is in you and me, for the oceans will drown all others.

16. And God's design was that although the inundation would greatly multiply her sorrows, she would even so bring forth children, as her love would be for her husband, and his for her.

17. And unto Adam it was God's will that he heed the words of his daughter, and God's warning that though they be descendants of the original mankind of the motherland, they should leave, as its destiny was Nature berserk, and if they stayed, surely they would regret it;

18. And where Adam was to go, the land would be difficult to farm, with thorns and thistles abounding; and even so the herb of the field was to be their food.

19. By his own toil and sweat he was destined to fight for survival after the inundation, even to the end of his days, when he would return to mother Earth, as it was Earth man came from, and unto Earth he shall return.

20. And after the inundation, Adam therefore made the woman his wife, and called her Eve, as she was to be the mother of all living from the motherland.

21. And, again after the inundation, as they were in a colder climate, it was God's design as part of their survival that they make coats of skins, and be clothed.

22. And it was God's design that Adam should take with him the knowledge of good and evil from the motherland as he put forth and left in order to live;

23. Therefore, in accordance with God's will, he left the Garden of Eden, to survive and live from the soil where he was to go.

24. So the man left; and the Garden of Eden was subjected to a cataclysm of earthquake and earth-fire, and the motherland lost its foundations and sank beneath the oceans.

CATACLYSMS REVISITED

The last cataclysm, known as Noah's flood, is pretty easy to study. It was the start of the New Stone Age, brought about by conditions following the last inundation, when even basic requirements for living were no longer available. Since then, uniformitarian geology has been allowed by Nature to continue on its path uninterrupted. Thousands of legends arose.

Two cataclysms ago, roughly 10,500 years ago, which we now know to be Adam and Eve's flood, was the start of the Old Stone Age. You can find these two last stone ages in almost any Junior High School general science textbooks. There again, this stone age was induced by the total lack of basic requirements for living. It's extremely difficult to find data from the era between the last two cataclysms, but it's there. Plus, of course, uniformitarian geology pursued its normal path between cataclysms. Era history is all legendary.

Three cataclysms ago, roughly 18,500 years ago, left little data for us. It is mentioned in Genesis 11:4. Shanidar Cave in Iraq gives us the best data of all; it's discussed in the text of this book.

Four cataclysms ago, about 29,000 years ago, was the end of the Wisconsin era, and we find more data than we do for the third-ago cataclysm.

Five cataclysms ago, 43,800 years ago, was derived by Jess Hale, a super mathematician. It's a real search.

Slowly, painstakingly, we are still putting the pieces of the puzzle together. The more pieces we find which fit into the picture, the more pieces are thrown on the table for us; and the more colorful and dramatic the picture becomes.

Did you understand that there are three cataclysms recorded in the Bible? Noah's, Adam and Eve's, and the one before that? If you missed it, check Genesis II.

I wish we had the funds to dig and search for three years in Tiahuanaco. A small idea of what could be found in this prehistoric city of South America can be gained by reading two books which I have mentioned before, but will again: The Calendar of Tiahuanaco and The Great Idol of Tiahuanaco, both by tremendous researchers, Hans Schindler Bellamy and Peter Allan. The conclusions drawn by Bellamy and Allan in these monumental works are startlingly close to mine: the city has lived through at least three epochs between cataclysms, the oldest ending about 11,500 years ago, terminating -with a cataclysm - the period in its history when it was at sea level, and starting a period of about 5,000 years during which it was at the bottom of the Pacific; then an upheaval during the cataclysm of about 7,000 years ago when it, along with its ocean bed, was raised to its present altitude of 12,500 feet. That cataclysm produced Noah's flood, gave birth to Niagara Falls, started the Ohio River flowing into the Mississippi, started the Neolithic stone age, raised the level of the oceans more than two hundred feet all over the world, initiated the era of modern history all over our planet - such as that of Greece, India, and Egypt -and gave birth to The Epic of Gilgamesh, containing the story of Noah's flood written by a Sumerian thousands of years before the Hebrews wrote about it in Genesis.

Each cataclysm is like a giant hand sweeping across the countryside, leaving its fingerprints for us to find amongst the elephant footprints of science in our search for the solution to this consuming mystery.

These fingerprints are well hidden amongst the heavy footprints of uniformitarian evidence. The two disciplines - uniformitarian geology and cataclysmology - have no real contest between them; each has its own place in science, for they complement each other, and actually a marriage of the two schools is in order.

Some of the cataclysmic fingerprints have been mentioned in Chapter II. Let's discuss them in more detail.

The story of frozen mammoths is intriguing indeed. No frozen mammoth was ever found in ice; all were found in frozen, homogenous muck. It used to be that you could buy frozen mammoth steaks in Alaskan restaurants, the meat had been so well preserved by quick-freezing in the muck after the mammoths' drowning and suffocating to death, then maintaining that frozen status for almost seven thousand years.

Perhaps the most noted of the thousands found thusly is the Beresovka mammoth, found near the Beresovka River in northern Siberia. Like all mammoths found wherein some comment was made concerning the skull, it was noted that his skull was pink from hemorrhaging in the head, plus the fact that he had a penile erection, both of these facts being evidence sufficient to prove that he suffocated to death in the surrounding homogenous muck. Further, he was frozen so fast and kept frozen for almost seven thousand years during which his erection was kept "on frozen record" constantly until he was found.

The Beresovka mammoth was found about 1900, and more scientific data was gathered and recorded about this animal than any other such frozen behemoth. It's true that this beast also has initiated more scientific controversy than any other such find. To my way of thinking, one man's work stands far above all others: Ivan T. Sanderson, the biologist. He approached the problem from a frozen foods viewpoint - and was the only one to do so.

This is his story:

When you freeze meat, the problem is to freeze it last enough so the moisture contained in the meat does not have time to form into large crystals while freezing.

The faster the freeze, the smaller the crystals. If you freeze meat too slowly, the moisture will form crystals large enough to destroy the fibrous structure of the meat; when defrosted, the meat will be nothing more than a mass of goo, unfit to cook or eat. The larger the piece of meat to be frozen, the more difficult it is to freeze it fast enough to avoid formation of the destructive moisture crystals, for heat must be removed at the same rate from, say, half a steer as from half a pound of ground meat. It would be the same problem if you had to freeze a bucket or tub of water in the same time it takes to freeze a thimbleful.

Now a mammoth weighs up to five tons. Those mammoths found in Siberia were somewhat smaller, but still several-ton animals. When the Beresovka mammoth was dissected by Russian scientists in 1901, they recorded that even the innermost lining of the beast's stomach had a perfectly preserved fibrous structure, indicating that his body heat had been removed by some super-prodigious process in nature.

Sanderson, taking special notice of this one point, took the problem to the American Fozen Foods Institute: What does it take to freeze an entire mammoth so that the moisture content of even the innermost parts of his body, even to the inner lining of his stomach, do not have time enough to form crystals large enough to destroy the meat's fibrous structure? The Institute really attacked this problem. To freeze a quarter or half a steer presented a big enough problem - but a whole mammoth!

Some weeks later the Institute went back to Sanderson with the answer: It's utterly impossible. With all of our scientific and engineering knowledge, there is absolutely no known way to remove the body heat from a carcass as big as a mammoth fast enough to freeze it without large moisture crystals forming in the meat. Furthermore, after exhausting the scientific and engineering techniques, they looked to nature and concluded that there is no known process in nature which could accomplish the feat. So many have loosely claimed that the Beresovka mammoth "fell in a crevasse" or "fell in the ice" or some such nonsense. There is absolutely, positively, irrevocably no explanation in the known processes of nature to explain the quick-freezing of the Beresovka mammoth - concurrently with the muck in which he was suffocated and drowned.

The Institute did tell Sanderson what it takes to do the job, however. First of all, the body temperature of the mammoth must be lowered about 140 degrees Fahrenheit (or 78 degrees Centigrade) from its normal temperature, and it must be accomplished in an absolute outside time limit of approximately four hours. Actually, they concluded, the freezing process would have to lake place in an elapsed time of closer to two hours.

The Institute did not take into account the effect on their conclusions which two other factors would have made: first, the fact that an entire strata of muck was frozen concurrently with the mammoth; and second, the fact that his erection had been preserved by quick freezing. The second of these facts reduces our actual freezing time to far below two hours. All that two to four hours represents is the outer limit of time within which the freezing process had to have taken place for no large moisture crystallization to have formed deep in the meat. The second fact tells us that the freezing time, at least for the entire strata of muck and the outer parts of the mammoth, had to be less than one minute, or perhaps more like half a minute.

The whole process bespeaks of an inhuman, supernatural violence: one foreleg, some ribs, and its pelvis were fractured (Do you realize what it takes to break a mammoth's foreleg and his pelvic bone!?); he was buried in a sea of muck formed by supersonically moving water, gathering and homogenizing the muck; suffocated and drowned in the muck, and quick frozen in the muck in an utterly impossible sequence of events - but nonetheless the process was performed - then kept frozen and preserved for almost seven thousand years.

Thank goodness for the scientific and intellectual curiosity of the Russian Czar who assigned the scientific team the responsibility to form the expedition into the far outreaches of eastern Siberia and bring back a thorough scientific analysis of this new-found mammoth near the Beresovka River. Today that same mammoth is mounted in a museum in Moscow. I believe I am correct in stating that it was the first time such a large animal was ever mounted by a taxidermist (or a team of taxidermists).

Where did the muck come from which buried the mammoth alive? This frozen mud can be found all over northern Siberia and Alaska. In

Alaska the frozen blanket ranges from twenty to ninety feet thick. Where we have been able to study this frozen tundra more closely, here in the United States, the evidence shows that the supernatural violence included supersonic winds, volcanic eruption, swift inundation creating the muck, a sudden temperature change to far below subzero freezing, and a precipitous total environmental climatic change. The muck comes from the inundation waters moving so swiftly and in such fantastic quantities that the water picks up all kinds of earth, mixes and homogenizes it with the water, then lays it down in a muck layer. Vivid descriptions of this layer of frozen muck are given by Prof. Frank C. Hibben in his book, The Lost Americans.

One of the best places to study many layers of muck laid down by many succeeding cataclysms is in the walls of the Grand Canyon, or in the Badlands of North Dakota. If you stand on the north rim of the Grand Canyon, pick one strata to follow, and trace it with your eyes as far as you can see in all directions - including the spires jutting upward in the canyon - you will find that strata homogenous from top to bottom, everywhere as it goes, laid down with uniform thickness, and sharply demarcated from the layers above and below it. Furthermore, if you happen to pick a layer that contains gravel, rocks and boulders interspersed through it, you will observe that ossified muck, gravel, rocks, and boulders are distributed throughout the layer quite evenly in all directions.

There is absolutely only one way for each layer to have been laid down so evenly and so homogenously, and that is all at once. All other hypotheses fall into oblivion in light of the homogeneity factor. This conclusion of the suddenness of the deposit, based on the homogeneity factor, is strengthened further by the flatness, uniformity of thickness, the independent character of each layer, and the sharp demarcation between any two adjacent layers.

Anyone in the earth-moving business who looks at these strata with the suddenness of deposit of each layer in mind will immediately realize that there is absolutely no way to accomplish this feat through any known means of engineering - nor is there any known way in the ordinary processes of nature to move that much earth, homogenize it - even with rocks and boulders if necessary - and deposit it all at once over uncountable square miles of surface in one single, flat, homogenous, even-depth layer. The only way possible is for cubic miles upon cubic miles of water to move at speeds into the supersonic range over continents, pick up earth - dirt, rocks and boulders - in unbelievable quantities, mix it with the water into a watery mud, have every rock and boulder grind each other into rounded off shapes as if they were pebbles, and finally deposit it all at once over huge areas of land in an even, flat layer of "homogenized" muck, rocks, and boulders which later dries out, and through the ages sometimes ossifies, such as in continents frozen in polar zones.

For many years I searched and hunted for evidence of what I call "sloshing" of fast-moving muck water as it becomes trapped in a huge basin. In the late 1980's I found a treasure trove of sloshing evidence in the part of Arizona and Utah known as Monument Valley. Never have I been so impressed with the beauty of Nature as I was when first viewing the Monument treasures of that valley. It's hard to believe that such beauty can come from the unimaginable violence of a cataclysm pounding on a landscape which would not exist were it not for the many cataclysms before the last one, each contributing its share toward the structure as we see it today, with thick layers upon other layers mixed with thinner layers after thinner ones, each with its own unique color and characteristics, with sharp demarcations between all layers.

There are also similar layers in Canyon de Chelly, southeast of Monument Valley a few miles.

The thick layers, approximately 60 to 80 feet thick, provided the sloshing evidence. Even though each of these thick layers showed definite evidence of having been deposited all at once, each layer with its own color and integral appearance, there was a diagonal sublayer - grain flow within each layer - tilted about twenty degrees off horizontal, with an adjacent sublayer tilted in the opposite direction both above and below it. These tilted sublayers, in comprising some very thick layers, were stacked upon each other in fifteen sublayers, all the same thickness, and each tilted in opposite directions from the layers adjacent to itself.

This evidence, then, finally provided the proof that sloshing does occur in a cataclysm. As the rapidly moving muck water sloshed back and forth across the valley, it deposited a little of itself with each slosh; it was moving so fast as to deposit the same amount of itself with each slosh, the total being so homogenized that each sublayer has the same characteristics as each and every one above and below it. Only the grain structure varies in slant with each sublayer. This structure is evident in miles upon miles of surrounding wails of the valley as well as in the monuments therein.

Before leaving Monument Valley, I'd like to tell you about one special place in the eastern part of the valley, Mexican Hat. It's a small town sitting next to the San Joaquin River, with a short plateau on the other side of the river. On the other side of the plateau rises the most unusual mountainside in the world, as many geologists have declared who have come to Mexican Hat from all over the world just to see that mountainside. It rises about 2,000 feet into the sky, with all of the grandeur of many sedimentary stratifications, large and small, in evidence. The unique feature of the whole mountainside is that the sedimentary layers all bend over down toward the river as if they were trying to flow into it and disappear. Thousands and thousands of feet of sedimentary strata are bent over toward and into the river in this fashion.

This scene is one of the most dramatic I have ever seen, proving the super violence that occurs during a cataclysm. In this case, a huge fissure opened in the Earth where the San Joaquin River flows now, the fissure being opened enough to be as a huge jaw opening to its throat with the molten layer normally sixty miles beneath. Of course, the molten layer would use into the sixty-mile throat, being sixty miles below that of seething white-hot molten everything beneath. The sixty-mile thick shell presses down, while also providing a huge fissure for that pressure to push the molten stuff upward into the gaping throat-fissure.

Now we have the most awesome, horrific, appalling, formidable, terrifying, uncanny, ultimately violent, paroxysmic, cataclysmic collision of the forces of Nature on the surface of our planet - even beyond imagination until you see for yourself, right at Mexican Hat, with the side of that mountain stopped cold in the midst of its death throes.

At this point the supersonically rampaging oceans and wind hit the scene. So, we have a super earthquake so huge as to open a fissure in the whole shell of the earth, opening a path for the molten layer below to be pressed upward into the fissure; the molten invader melting the hard layer beneath that side of the mountain; the 1,000 mile-per-hour oceanwater slaughtering the mountainside (having lost its foundations), driving it down into the huge fissure and steaming the molten stuff below into solidity; and the mountainside stops feeding itself downward into the maw, while the oceans in their fury pass on, leaving a huge

97

part of themselves sloshing around and back and forth in the valley, plus some surviving, beautiful, picturesque monuments standing today for us to see.

In other parts of the valley, upheavals of sedimentary strata in huge structures point upward, with the rock being scorched in a plethora of places. Church Rock and Agathla reign; each has many scorched sedimentary boulders scattered around, near its base.

I have read geologists' reports, and have been told by Wayne, one of the tour guides at Monument Valley Lodge (one of the nicest places to stay) that he has read geologists' reports, all telling of lava flows in Monument Valley. I have spent time through several years in Monument Valley, searching from one end to the other and even beyond the valley, for any evidences of lava. I have never found any evidence anywhere of even a suggestion of lava. All I ever could find was scorched sedimentary rock, which, from a distance, could have fooled anyone into thinking it was lava rock. I have seen dark scorched rock in abandoned gold mines near Pike's Peak, which scorching occurred during a cataclysm when the heat from the 60mile molten layer broke through fissures in the 60-mile thick hard outer shell of the Earth, scorching the rocks in that shell.

Going back to the oceans of water, mixing with earth and rocks and laying down layers and sloshing sublayers of sediment, a good measure of the speed with which the water must move over the land is provided for us by the granite blocks on the eastern slopes of the Jura Mountains in France. DeLuc Sr., Von Buch, DeLuc Jr., and DeSaussure give us much information through their early geological observations of the dispersion of the Alpine granite blocks through the mountains, valleys and lakes of Italy, Switzerland und France. Even Bakewell, through his early dissenting observations, lends more credence to the fast-moving water conclusions of the other men because of the looseness of his arguments.

The great Swiss geologist Escher gave the most credence to the fast-moving water argument through his observations, which support the earliest concepts set forth by J. Andre DeLuc Jr. in the 1820's.

Let us envision the Jura Mountains as if we were looking down from an airplane. First of all we'd notice that they are similar to the Allegheny Mountains in Pennsylvania, for they look like a giant, wrinkled-up carpet with rolling ridges running from northeast to southwest; the Swiss-French border follows the same direction in the middle of the range. You can also see that the ridges have passes through them here and there, so that a person on the ground can see northwest through one ridge to the southeastern slope of the next ridge in many places.

It's a well-known fact that the Jura Mountains are non-granitic. Whatever granite exists in those mountains is still buried deep in them; they are largely calcareous. However, on the southeastern slopes of the ridges there are countless granite blocks sitting on the surface. These blocks, each weighing tons upon tons, have been traced to the Swiss Alps, across the Swiss valley to the southeast. If you look several ridges to the northwest in the Juras, you will find the granite blocks only on the southeastern slope of the ridge, and clustered only opposite passes through the ridge adjacent to the southeast. These blocks sit on the slope at an altitude the same as where they came from in the Alps of Italy and Switzerland, 50 to 80 miles across the valley from Switzerland to where they were deposited on the Juras.

In order for them to be found on the southeastern slopes of the Juras where they are, a tremendous upheaval of granite in the Italian-Swiss Alps had to occur during some cataclysmic violence, followed by water moving at such fantastic speeds as to sweep the mighty blocks of granite from 50 to 80 miles across Switzerland, over the Juras, through the passes and deposit them in clusters against the southeastern slopes of the inner ridges of the Juras.

It fits perfectly with the picture of supernatural violence uncovered by Prof. Frank C. Hibben in his studies of shredded and dismembered prehistoric animals in Alaska, buried and quick-frozen in and with muck, together with twisted, torn, burned and quick-frozen trees.

Hibben states that one necessary force in the contributing factors is supersonic winds. The only way of generating such winds over tremendous areas is to move the land in such a way as to depart from its normal west-to-east daily rotation so the atmosphere, continuing its normal daily rotation, will then be moving at supersonic speeds relative to the land over which it is moving.

Now in the Earth's normal rotation, the oceans also rotate West to East one revolution per day. When a cataclysm occurs, the 60-mile thick shell of the Earth slips in a direction differing from that of its normal rotation; the atmosphere continues its normal rotational direction; and the oceans also refuse to change their rotational direction. So, the atmosphere and oceans proceed to move over land masses which are passing underneath them in a new direction - some of the oceans and air moving at supersonic speeds with respect to the land moving in a different direction underneath. With oceans moving over land masses at such speeds, it's easy to understand how the huge granite blocks were moved from the Alps to the Juras while losing little or no altitude, and how cubic miles of earth can be picked up, mixed with water and homogenized, then laid down in an even, flat, independent layer such as we find exposed in the walls of the Grand Canyon, Monument Valley and Canyon de Chelly.

Further, we can understand how the irresistibly, overwhelmingly annihilating force of the waters moving at utterly unbelievable speeds can, in the blink of an eye, obliterate entire civilizations and every vestige of anything they ever accomplished. Even in our times there have been occasions when a simple dam's breaking and releasing its waters over a small town below literally wiped out every splinter of evidence of the town and people having been there.

One of the fingerprints which the cataclysmic giant hand leaves, telling us of this supernatural violence on the Earth, is the plethora of mammalian teeth of many, many species found in the sharp demarcation boundaries between sedimentary layers such as we see exposed in the Grand Canyon. It bespeaks of animal life being pulverized, with teeth the only mammalian substance hard enough to withstand the onslaught.

Some places undergo less violent winds and inundation, to be sure; and there we find traces of prehistoric civilizations which had advanced to achievements we deem impossible for that many years ago. Let's go back to Tiahuanaco, in South America, to see what's there.

The Incas discovered this deserted city at 12,500 feet altitude on the shores of Lake Titicaca, in the second century A.D. Although they lived in that land lor generations upon generations, centuries after centuries, they left it totally undisturbed. Anyone who has been on a hunt for gold or treasure in the mountains - as I have been in New Mexico - knows the Indian credo: "What is in the mountain belongs to the mountain." That means that whatever they find they do not disturb nor destroy, nor move nor remove.

You can read about it, see it portrayed in movies, or be told about it, but there is nothing like seeing it in person when gold fever takes over an entire personality.

It's a kind of consummate greed which changes a veteran outdoorsman to a wild-eyed, scheming, secretive, intense introvert who could lead himself and others to destruction and death through his greed. I have seen it.

Tiahuanaco was found by Pizarro and his band of plunderers in the 1520's. The gold fever had evidently taken over his entire expedition of 13 to 16 men, for they proceeded to vandalize almost everything in sight. They smashed thousands of statues searching for gold. There were huge silver bolts of up to several tons each, passing through massive stone monoliths. You guessed it: they broke up the monoliths in order to obtain the silver bolts.

There was one member of the early discoverers, a Spanish priest, Diego de Alcabaso, who wrote down what he saw: "I saw a vast hall carved on its roof to represent thatch. There were the waters of a lake which washed the walls of a splendid court in this city of the dead, and, standing in its fine court, in the shallows of the water, on the platform of a superb colonnade were many fine statues of men and women. So real they were that they seemed to be alive. Some had goblets and upraised drinking-cups. Others sat, or reclined, as in life. Some walked in the stream flowing by the ancient walls. Women, carved in stone, dandled babies in their laps, or bore them on their backs. In a thousand natural postures, people stood or reclined."

Not one of these statues stands today. The greed of civilization has literally devastated Tiahuanaco with vandalism and thievery.

However, vandals through the centuries who visited this fabulous storehouse of prehistory did what most do who have the treasure fever - they ignored the intellectual values which were less obvious. The great stone gate in the temple of Kalasasaya has inscriptions across its arch and on its pillars which, to the untrained eye, appear to be but meaningless picture carvings. It remained for Arthur Posnanski to realize its importance; he was followed by Wendell Bennett and John Phillips; then Hans Schindler Bellamy and Peter Allan completed the picture with their brilliant deciphering and translation of the pictures, so aptly described in their book, The Calendar of Tiahuanaco. Their later book, The Great Idol of Tiahuanaco, evinces further their brilliance in deciphering and translating the picture symbols carved in a monolithic statue excavated from a buried temple. This book not only explains their deciphering and translating, but tells of the arduous work performed in order to preserve the tremendous monolith. The only thing they don't explain is why this huge statue has two left hands and no right hand!

The works of Bellamy and Allan show many things concerning the calendar and time standards of Tiahuanaco in two different epochs, probably the Caspian and Hudson Bay eras. The details and differences between hours, days and years then and now I shall leave to those who wish to read those books. The main point of their discussion which should be noted here is that the Idol and the Calendar both recorded that, during both eras, a retrograde moonsatellite orbited around the Earth. During the Idol's era -probably 29,000 to 18,500 years ago - the satellite was approximately 24,150 miles from the Earth; and during the Calendar Gate's era - probably 18,500 to 11,500 years ago - the satellite was approximately 23,360 miles from the Earth.

Obviously the moon-satellite was far closer to our planet than our present moon. Obviously it passed the Roche limit of approximately 8,000 miles from the Earth and disintegrated, accounting for many legends of prehistory of terrible impacts with the Earth by asteroids or comets.

Where did the moon-satellite come from? How did our planet capture it? And, of course, where did our present moon-satellite come from? When did our planet capture it? And how and why did it happen? If Tiahuanaco and its moon-satellite are to make any sense for us, these questions must be answered.

The Bode-Titius relationship may give us a key to the answer. Titius and Bode, two German astronomers, individually, concurrently, discovered this relationship in the eighteenth century. If we take orbit numbers, or ring numbers, of the planets through Saturn the ring numbers being 0, 1,2, 4, 8, 16, 32, multiply each number by 3, add 4 to each result, divide each by 10, the series becomes 0.4, 0.7, 1.0, 1.6, 2.8, 5.2, and 10.0. These numbers, excepting and skipping 2.8, represent the relative distances of the then known planets from the Sun - Mercury, Venus, Earth, Mars, 2.8, Jupiter, and Saturn - with 2.8 representing no known planet at that time for that distance.

When the planet Uranus was discovered in 1781, it fit right into the series at 19.6; the "law" seemed strengthened, and an intense search was initiated for anything that might be at the 2.8 distance. In 1801 the little planetoid Ceres was discovered at 2.8; by 1945 more than 1,500 more were found on the same orbit. It has been well established as the ring of minor planets, or planetoids, or asteroids.

In 1846 the planet Neptune was discovered - and it seemed to disobey the rules set down by the Bode-Titius relationship. It should have been at 38.8 on the relative distance scale - but it was closer to 29.2.

In 1930 the planet Pluto was discovered, and the Bode-Titius "law" seemed to fall apart completely. Pluto was found close to 38.8, where Neptune was supposed to be, whereas the "law" seemed to indicate that Pluto should be at 77.2.

Since that time the relationship, commonly known as "Bode's Law", has been regarded in astronomy as nothing more than an insignificant curiosity.

Perhaps a new look at Bode's Law is in order. If so much of it is correct, then the part of it which appears to be erroneous seems to be so only because of our lack of understanding of the basics involved.

First, instead of using relative numbers, we shall work with ring numbers, or orbit numbers. The first progression (0, 1,2, 4, 8, 16, 32, etc.) represents these numbers. Also, instead of this progression - which is geometric except for the zero - let's fill in all of the numbers, making a true arithmetic progression. The numbers will be 0, 1,2, 3, 4, 5, 6, 7, 8, - so on to 256.

Now in this progression the ring numbers 0, 1,2, 4, 8, 16, 32, 64, 128, and 256 can be regarded as fundamental rings. All other rings can be regarded as harmonic rings. Between any two fundamentals, the ring which lies halfway between is the first harmonic; any ring which lies halfway between a fundamental and a first harmonic is a second harmonic; any ring halfway between a second harmonic and a first harmonic, or halfway Between a second harmonic and a fundamental, is a third harmonic, and so on.

The next step is to label the ring numbers with the planets as they are actually positioned in the Solar System. We can simplify the table if we take all of the ring numbers up to 8; then only the fundamentals, 1st, and second harmonics beyond that to Uranus; then the fundamentals, 1st, 2nd, & 3rd harmonics to ring 256.

The first thing that we notice is that all of the planets are on fundamentals except Neptune. It's the only planet which is on a harmonic ring, as it appears on the first harmonic 96 between Uranus and Pluto, which are on fundamentals 64 and 128 respectively.

Now we come to another discovery. The number of rings between the planets increases the farther away from the Sun the planets are, until it appears that the maximum number of rings possible between planets is 3 1. On each

32nd ring there has to be a planet whether the ring is a fundamental or a harmonic. That's why Neptune is on the 96th ring, a 1st harmonic, the 32nd ring under Uranus, with Pluto on the 128th ring, a fundamental, the 32nd ring after Neptune.

Something else appears apparent also: When the Solar System was born, planets tried to be born on each ring. Full-blown planets were born on every fundamental, and on any ring 31 rings away from any harmonic ring 31 rings away from any other planet. On all other rings, minor planets were born, or a ring of planetoids. Since there are four major planets inside the ring of planetoids on 8, let's assume that the entire Solar System is made up of three groups of four major planets plus a ring of planetoids in each group. This means that there may be two more undiscovered planetoid rings, 112 and 240. If we look at the minor planet rings on either side of Jupiter, and apply Kepler's laws to them, we find that the moons of Jupiter - even the retrograde ones - are explained as captured minor planets from both inside and outside harmonic rings around Jupiter.

Before we examine the results of our construction, let's look into the outer regions of the Solar System: Ring 256 is where the comets turn around and head back into the heart of the system. Further, it is known that there is more than one planet outside Pluto; our table tells us that there should be three planets on rings 160, 192, and 224. The total number of rings tells us that there is a fantastic number of captured and uncaptured minor planets yet to be discovered. The junk of the Solar System!

Let's look at the abbreviated table of the Solar System - the first orderly interpretation of Bode's Law. Ring 256 appears to be where the Sun's belt of protons is. The belt must exist, since the Sun's magnetic field is bipolar; furthermore, it has to be outside the planets.

Planet	Fund.	1st Harm.	2nd Harm.	3rd Harm.
		Ring Numbers		
Mercury	0			
Venus	1			
Earth	2			
Moon		3		
Mars	4			
Phobos			5	
Deimos		6		
Lost			7	
Planetoids #1	8			
			10	
		12		
			14	
Jupiter	16			
			20	
		24		
			28	
Saturn	32			
			40	
		48		
			56	
Uranus	64			
				72
			80	
				88
Neptune		96		
				104
Planetoids #2			112	
				120
Pluto	128			
				144
X1			160	
				176
X2		192		
				208
X3			224	
Planetoids #3				240
?	256	(Solar Inner Radiation Belt?)		

It's apparent that our present moon was created on ring 3, Phobos on 5, and Deimos on 6. Ring 7 is vacant. That presents a real challenge. Whatever happened to the minor planet from Ring 7?

The closeness of Phobos and Deimos to Mars tells us that rings 4, 5, and 6 closed together a tremendous amount, most probably through a succession of events in the Solar System causing the series of cataclysms on Earth. It's logical that ring 7 also would have closed toward Mars' ring so that Mars would have captured the minor planet from Ring 7 as well as Phobos and Deimos. Once orbiting around Mars, "Lost" could have come close enough to Earth to be stolen from Mars by Earth and be the moon-satellite so well described on the Idol and Calendar Gate of Tiahuanaco. Further, the closeness of that satellite to Earth would be justification for the premise that "Lost" was stolen by Earth from Mars.

The multitude of legends springing from the cataclysm of 11,500 years ago about "Venus moving into orbit" or "Venus changing her orbit" most probably describe the capture of our present moon from Ring 3 - which in its day, eons ago, evidently was a pretty fair planet with radiation belts orbiting around the Sun.

In any case, the now vacant Ring 7, the records from Tiahuanaco of a retrograde-orbiting moon, the plethora of impact craters on the moon and Mars, and the mountains of dense material buried in the mantle of the Earth as uncovered by perturbed orbits in our manmade satellites, and Bode's Law, expanded here to include orbits of both fundamentals and harmonics, now offer an orderly meaning to us.

Instabilities in the Solar System which lead to capture of minor planets by major planets may seem impossible or improbable; however, if we consider one minor instability in the Solar System, in the Earth's rotation, we can believe that major changes in stability are possible. You can find it in Encyclopaedia Britannica: mention is made of two astronomically abrupt changes in the Earth's rotation within the last hundred years. This planet of ours is not an inertial body - it's a complex motor-generator system, as are the Solar System, the Milky Way Galaxy, its parent supergalaxy, and the Universe in which we live. Realize also that astronomers of Tiahuanaco recorded stability changes on the Calendar Gate and the Great Idol.

In light of the fantastic stonework in Tiahuanaco characterizing the civilization which ended abruptly about 11,500 years ago, we can look at other great prehistoric works in stone which stand as mysterious monumental memorials to lost engineering techniques. There is Baalbek, in Lebanon - formerly known as Heliopolis - where three huge stones are fitted together to make a platform 300 feet long. The mate to the largest stone still lies in a quarry southwest of town. That mate, believe it or not, weighs over 1,200 tons! What fantastic event would cause this prehistoric civilization to leave its tools figuratively hanging in midair? And prehistoric Sacsahuaman, Peru, where a 20,000 ton monolithic block of stone lies with its steps upside down, overturned by some prehistoric, supernatural wrath of nature; and there, as immobile as the silent boom of the kettle drums of eternity and space, stand walls of incredibly fitted huge stones.

We hear so much about the stone statues of Easter Island. There is also a wall of gigantic, precisely fitted stones, suggestive of the same civilization as Sacsahuaman and Baalbek. Giant stone statues are not exclusive to Easter Island; they can be found in the Tuamoto Archipelago, on Nukuhiva, Fatuhiva, Rivavae, and Pitcairn; and in Colombia, Ecuador, Peru, and Bolivia. Those statues on Easter Island which were buried up to their necks and recently excavated showed a geological environment the significance of which eluded the excavators. The lessons learned from the stratas in the Grand Canyon, Monument Valley, and Canyon de Chelly teach us to look for homogeneity - and there it is in the dirt walls of the excavations around the gigantic statues. They were all buried at once in a colossal inundation. It appears to be the reason for the tools being figuratively left in midair in the quarries of Easter Island as well as those in Baalbek.

Mother Nature performs her own works in stone which can serve as time-clocks for us. Take Niagara Falls, for instance. When the falls first started, the river flowed over a cliff where the mouth of the gorge below the falls is today. There was no gorge. As the years went by the water broke away the cliff bit by bit, year by year, century by century, to form the seven-mile long gorge which reposes below the falls today. For the past 100 years the breakaway of the Canadian Falls has averaged approximately 4.5 feet per year. When the falls were young - when the gorge's first 2 to 3 miles or so were being carved out by the river - the breakaway was faster since the falls were narrower, the depth of water passing over the cliff deeper, and the height of the cliffs greater. A reasonable early breakaway figure would be 6.0

to 6.1 feet per year, which would make the age of the falls and gorge below them about 7,000 years - the birth of both falls and gorge coinciding with oceanographic data which tells us that the oceans all over the world took a sudden rise of over 200 feet, and stayed risen, gradually lowering in height since then to their levels of today.

St. Anthony's Falls in the upper Mississippi River in Minnesota bears another telltale story in Nature's series of recording time-clocks. The gorge below those fills is 8 miles long; over the past century the breakaway has averaged 5.5 feet per year. If we repeat the same reasoning processes that we used in analyzing the gorge below Niagara Falls, we come up with the same figure for the age of St. Anthony's Falls and the gorge below them: approximately 7,000 years.

These datings, plus others - such as the eruption of lava around the Pyramid of Cuicuilco in Mexico -lead us to a date of the last cataclysm

(Noah's flood) of somewhere around 7,000 years ago.

Earlier datings - 11,500 years ago for the abrupt end of the Laurentian Basin ice cap in Canada and the ice cap in southwestern Australia, plus the same date for the jamming burial of countless animals, fish, mammals, birds, and humans in the Pejark Marsh in southeastern Australia, plus the same date for the abrupt end of civilization in Tiahuanaco by an inundation, plus scientific data from all over the world showing an abrupt worldwide climatic change at the same time, establish 11,500 years ago as a close estimate for Adam and Eve's cataclysm, the one preceding Noah's flood. If we accept Tiahuanacan dating, it was approximately 11,560 years ago.

Isn't it interesting that the "new stone age" and the "old stone age" datings coincide with the times of Noah's cataclysm and Adam and Eve's cataclysm? It is plain that each cataclysm leaves this planet with less than one percent of all life surviving; and those meager spots all over the world where some humans survive, what is left for them to live by and with? Who has even a shovel? Whatever clothes they have, how short a time those clothes will last! You can understand how each day, the entire day, total effort is spent in finding food (as in plant food), hunting and fishing, just to survive. The fight for survival is as extreme as it is unimaginable. Most of those who survive cannot teach language, ethics, mathematics, history, government, or anything of what we regard as classical education. If there are children, Dad tells his kids all about the inundation, and they believe him, because he is their Dad. By the time there are grandchildren, they don't believe a word he says,

because, well - um - you know - he has to be a little off his rocker to tell stories like that. In a matter of a few generations, the cataclysm becomes a verbal legend, because who has something to write with or on? And, of those who survive, who has the language skills it takes to write it even if he did have writing tools? Furthermore, who has time to write or teach anything when the top priority of each and every day is survival?

Let's go back to dating. Meager data shows the cataclysm previous to Adam and Eve's to be about 18,500 years ago; the previous one 29,000 years ago; and thanks to mathematician Jess Hale's structures of Nature, the previous one computes at 43,750 years ago. Mathematically, its function is that of a helicoid.

Of all of the correlations of data 1 regard one of the most striking to be that of Shanidar Cave in Iraq. The Smithsonian Institution expedition, headed by Ralph S. Solecki, and the Iraqui DirectorateGeneral of Antiquities shared in this work. Carbon-14 datings showed the boundaries between layers laid down by successive civilizations to be commensurate with the dates of cataclysms of 7,000, 11,500,

18,500 and 29,000 years ago; plus the incredible fact that no Carbon-14 was deposited in the cave during the Caspian Sea North Polar Era from 29,000 to 18,500 years ago. It is entirely logical, since the cave would have been so close to the North Pole as to plausibly have been closed off by a polar ice cap; consequently, no living matter could have entered the cave - and it takes living matter to absorb Carbon-14 for us to find and date. This crude cave is as much a memorial to the last four cataclysms as Tiahuanaco.

Speaking of memorials, has anyone ever lived through a cataclysm and written of his experience, leaving a personal memorial to the occasion? Of course! If we first look at Genesis, three cataclysms are mentioned there: Noah's inundation, the last one, 7,000 years ago; Adam and Eve's, 11,500 years ago; and the previous one of 18,500 years ago, barely mentioned in Genesis II, 4. Two other stories exist, and they are most intriguing. One is from

Noah's time, and the other in Adam and Eve's time - from Greece.

In 1849 Austen Henry Layard started excavating the mound of Kuyunjik on the banks of the Tigris River. It was there that he discovered the fabulous city of Ninevah, previously known only through the Old Testament. He discovered the palace built by the bloody emperor Sennacherib. Assurbanipal, a grandson of Sennacherib by one of his concubines, had added a library to the palace; he then sent emissaries out to comb his kingdom for original tablets worthy of being in his library, and had the emissaries borrow the tablets and bring them to the palace. Assurbanipal had exact copies made of each one, and returned the originals to their rightful owners. He had some 30,000 copies made on clay tablets, and put them all in his library. These were the tablets which Layard found.

Among the tablets were twelve comprising the Epic of Gilgamesh - a man who was, at that time, a legendary king of the first dynasty of Erech, closely following the great deluge. He has since been shown to have been a real human being.

Gilgamesh sought the secret of eternal life, driven to do so by the death of his friend Enkidu. He was told that he should find a man by the name of Utnapishtim, who had been granted eternal life by the gods.

He found Utnapishtim, whom Gilgamesh successfully persuaded to tell his story. Utnapishtim stated that indeed, he had been granted the secret of and was told by the gods:

"O man of Shuruppak, son of Ubar-Tutu,

Abandon wealth, scorn possessions, save thyself;

Tear down thy house, and build a ship;

Let it be well-measured.

He describes the ship he built, and from all principals of naval architecture, it was a ship which ocould not be tipped over - square! (Probably meaning oblong). After he built it, he launched it on no less than eight down cruises; each time he would bring it back, with bitumen, and check it out again. Finally he had it shipshape, so he held a real Belshazzar's feast to celebrate it⁵ completion, with beer, wine, mutton served to all who came.

Imagine this in your own neighborhood! Some of his neighbors must have thought he was a real nut.

On the very next day after the feast, he decided that it was time to load the ship and set it to sea on the cruise for his survival.

"I then loaded the ship.

The whole harvest of life I loaded

- My family, my friends,

The beasts of the field, the cattle of the field,

The craftsmen, and the tools of their trades -

I made them all embark.

I then embarked, and closed the door.

As soon as a gleam of dawn shone in the sky,
The skies darkened, black clouds gathered;
Inside them Adad thundered.

Soon all light had turned to darkness;

Brother could recognize brother no more,

The animals of the skies can no longer see each other."

Utnapishtim then describes the onslaught of the storm which generated sheer, all-out terror in the ship. Following that,

"For six days and nights

Wind and flood marched on,

The holocaustic wind overwhelmed the land.

When the seventh day dawned,

The ill wind was stilled; the oceans, - the flood -

Which had waged war like an army, was ceased. I opened the window, and beheld the devastation, And all mankind was turned into mud!

As high and as flat as the rooftops lay the swamp! And thousands of dead -

Of man, and beast, and cattle -

Lay floating in the mire!"

He then proceeded to describe the bumping into the mountain, the releasing of the three birds, the bringing back of the leaf; followed by disembarkation, the building of an altar, and more.

Addendum

Since going to press, an astronomer in Australia named Dr. Arthur Blesse has observed a progressing phenomenon which he has no idea is directly related to the next cataclysm. He has observed, through monthly measurements of the Sun's surface temperature over the past five years, that the Sun's temperature is decreasing at a rate which predicts that it will go completely out by 1999 or 2000. What he cannot predict is that it will reignite very shortly thereafter.

What he has discovered is an authentication of the start of the next cataclysm, predicted in The Adam and Eve Story through scientific rationale, and by Nostradamus, Cayce, and Scallion through clairvoyance.

What Dr. Blesse predicts actually is the short period of time of utter, utter darkness, with the Sun completely out, which Utnapishtim describes. It's interesting that Blesse authenticates the extremely unusual, black darkness which Utnapishtim describes as immediately following daybreak!

Undoubtedly the story is the primeval version of Noah's flood, written thousands of years ago, covering many generations before Ezra dictated his version to five scribes in reconstructing Genesis I, II, and III.

One of the most important things about it is that we have a firsthand, on-the-spot report of the laying down of a strata as we see exposed in the walls of the Grand Canyon, Monument Valley and Canyon de Chelly, with a vivid description of the terrorizing wind and inundation which are a part of the event. Language scholars say that for anyone to write such a description, he had to be there and see it with his own eyes.

More important also, the great archaeologist Leonard Woolley found Utnapishtim's rooftop-high layer of mud in the 1920's - by then clay, about nine feet thick - in the Tigris-Euphrates Rivers region; further, beneath it a civilization which was buried, and totally different from any found above it.

Of course, we have the more than 8,000 survival legends in the Malay Peninsula region as uncovered by the great legendary Fraser; we have other survival legends from the southwestern American Indians; and from Dine

Bajane, The Navajo Creation Story, by Paul G. Zolbrod, we have this striking legend:

"At the end of the fourth night as they were at last about to end their meeting, they all noticed something white in the east. They also saw it in the south. It appeared in the west, too. And in the north it also appeared.

It looked like an endless chain of white mountains. They saw it on all sides. It surrounded them, and they noticed it was closing in on them rapidly. It was a high, insurmountable wall of water! And it was flowing in on them from all directions, so that they could not escape neither to the east nor to the west; neither to the south nor to the north could they escape.

"So, having nowhere else to go, they took flight. Into the air they went. Higher and higher they soared, it is said."

From this description of flight, and from following parts of the legend, it is my interpretation that the entire legend is one from the cataclysm of 11,500 years ago. It would take years of work on my part to nail down the time of that one legend. I don't have years.

Let's take the story which we know is from two cataclysms ago. Historians tell us that for a 4,500 year period befo~re~ 7,000 years ago there is no written history from anywhere in the world. India, Greece, and Egypt follow this characteristic. It's interesting that 7,000 plus 4,500 equals 11,500 years ago, isn't it?

In light of the priests of Egypt telling Solon of a great antediluvian Hellenic civilization, let's take a look at the Greek alphabet. It is written today as it has been for all of written Greek history; but the pronunciation is not the same. In the time of Euclid, the pronunciation was changed to the "slang" of their time, it is told. Let's compare the modern and old:

Alpha	Alpaaha	Al-*pah*-ah-ha
Beta	Beta	*Bay*-tah
Gamma	Kamma	*Kahm*-ma
Delta	Telta	*Tell*-ta
Epsilon	Epsilonom	Ep-zill-*oan*-om
Zeta	Zeta	*Zay*-tah
Eta	Etha	*Ayt*-ha
Theta	Thethehaha	Thay-thay-*ha*-ha
Iota	Iota	Eye-*oh*-ta
Kappa	Kapaa	Kah-*pah*-ah
Lambda	Lambeta	*Lam*-bay-tah
Mu	Mu	Moo
Nu	Ni	Nee
Xi	Xi	Ksee
Omicron	Omikleon	Oh-mik-*lay*-on
Pi	Pi	Pie
Rho	Laho	*Lah*-hoe
Sigma	Zilkma	Zee-*ik*-ma
Tau	Tau	*Tah*-oo
Upsilon	Upazileon	*Oo*-pa-*zee*-lay-*ohn*
Phi	Pehi	*Pay*-high
Chi	Chi	Kigh
Psi	Pezi	*Pay*-zigh
Omega	Omecka	Oh-*mec*-kah

If you read the old pronunciations out loud, it sounds very much like Polynesian! Plausibly, it is a summation of prehistoric Mayan words, which we can translate into English. Here, then is the Greek alphabet:

Overwhelmingly break the oceans; They inundate the lands. Mother Earth receives the deep. Where obstructions are, shores form. Mighty winds rampage, where with oceans piling over oceans, they bury all that is living and moving. Where hills are, they vanish, buried, submerged with the earth of the motherland.

Mountain peaks alone stand forth before the onslaught on our planet which abates little by little until there comes the cold wind. The motherland is now at the bottom of the earth, an abyss, a vast reservoir of frozen mud. There comes out of volcanoes vapors pouring forth, with swirling smoke, and molten lava.

It appears that it tells the story of the cataclysm which ended the Laurentian Ice Age, started the old stone age, ended the Australian ice cap, and initiated the abrupt climatic change over the whole world as discovered in oceanography. Of course it was the cataclysm through which Adam and Eve survived, ending a civilization in the eastern hemisphere. Traces - wisps - of that civilization are found in the legends recorded by the Hindu historian Valmiki, and told by the Polynesian tribes such as the Maori.

The story apparently was handed down verbally, generation by generation, through the 5,000-year period of no written history; and, after Noah's - or Utnapishtim's - flood, when history started to be written, it became the basis for the Greek alphabet.

Factual, legendary, or mythological - or maybe even historical or semi-historical, whichever it may be, the story is fascinating, isn't it? If you wish to pursue it further, read Don Antonio Batres Jaurequi's History of Central America and James Churchward's The Lost Continent of Mu. Churchward makes many mistakes, but his works are interesting reading. His unexacting treatment of the Calendar Gate of Tiahuanaco makes one question his sometimes cursory methods.

History before the cataclysm of 11,500 years ago comes to us in the form of legends; we can understand those legends and their origins far better in light of the history of cataclysms. The Greek alphabet has existed in two forms through all of Greek history. Where did it come from before that? It appears that it is a direct descendant of prehistoric Mayan or Naga. Perhaps the answer lies in the megalyths, runes, and glyphs ranging from the Matto Grosso to Deutschland, Finland, England, and Friesland. All we can say at this time is that these are prehistoric secrets of the Hellenes!

Now we must leave the pleasures of enjoying our hypotheses and return to more serious considerations. Let's discuss the most elusive piece of the puzzle, the part which has taken twenty years to derive and fit into the puzzle: the trigger, the cause of cataclysms.

My thoughts go back to Georges Cuvier's challenge to the world of science which he wrote in 1812 "....discover the cause of these events." Dr. Hibben's contemporary adjunct to that challenge is really an inseparable part of it: "Any good solution to a consuming mystery must answer all of the facts."

As the years went by and we remained dissatisfied with our concepts concerning the trigger, we concentrated on that part of the puzzle. It has taken twenty years to find a satisfactory solution - one which answers all of the facts.

The fascinating work of the Swedish physicist Hannes Alfven lighted the tortuous path to the answer. In the 1950's he discovered a kind of energy which nobody even thought existed, which he labeled "magnetohydrodynamic" energy. Abbreviated, it's called mhd. Actually, it's a combination of magnetic, electrical, and physical forces.

It can be described best with what I call a "kitchen example". Suppose you took a glass cylinder containing mercury at room temperature - and everyone knows it's "molten" or liquid under those conditions. It's so dense that you can float a glass mirror on top of it. So let's do just that, and make some scratches on the mirror. If you shine a light down on the mirror, the light beam will reflect on the ceiling and show images of the scratches in the mirror on the ceiling.

Now let's put an agitator - like a miniature version of a washing machine agitator - in the bottom of the cylinder of mercury, with a shaft or axle going through the bottom of the cylinder, and fastened to the agitator. Let's put a handle on the end of the shaft sticking out of the bottom of the cylinder. We can twirl the agitator back and forth with the handle (slowly only, because the mercury is so dense and heavy) and agitate the mercury in the glass cylinder.

When we agitate the mercury in this fashion we find that the slipperiness of the mercury, atom to atom, is so great that all of the motion of the agitator is absorbed by the mercury before it ever reaches the top surface where the mirror is. The mirror won't budge.

If we wind a wire around the glass cylinder and connect it to a battery, we will have an electromagnet - following the same principles used in the doorbell of your home. There is an electrical current flowing around the cylinder, and a magnetic field going through the cylinder, end-to-end.

Now we find that things have changed. When we rotate the agitator back and forth, the mercury acts as if it were a plastic, or near-solid. The mirror makes all of the moves that the agitator does, showing that the mercury has lost its internal slipperiness, and is moving integrally as if it were almost solid.

Alfven tried a refined version of this experiment in his laboratory, and this is how the phenomenon was discovered. It was first reasoned that tiny electrical charges, called "eddy currents", were being generated in the mercury, which in turn were generating tiny local opposing magnetic fields, and this was causing the solidifying effect. He reasoned that if this were true, the larger the diameter he made the glass cylinder, the bigger the electrical current and the stronger the magnetic field would have to be to maintain the same physical force link between the agitator and mirror.

He built another agitator vessel with a larger diameter cylinder of mercury - and found the reverse to be true! The larger the diameter of the glass cylinder, the less magnetic field strength and electric current needed to maintain the physical force link between agitator and mirror. This seemingly broke all the rules of known Physics and Engineering.

Hannes Alfven realized that he had discovered the existence of a kind of energy, traveling from the agitator to the mirror, which was previously undetected by any scientist. His rigorous mathematical work in expanding James Clerk Maxwell's three ingenious equations for expressing electromagnetic radiation (radio broadcasts to you) showed that there were electrical, magnetic, and physical force fields acting as a combined field between the agitator and mirror.

Alfven expanded his mathematical research to show that space is literally a sea of mhd energy, and that, as weak as the magnetic field of any blue-white star is, it is strong enough to support an internal mhd energy structure within the star.

Alfven's work also applies to any planet with only one each North and South magnetic pole. 1 have built several earth current recording stations, and know from personal observation that Earth currents are strong enough to support our planet's inner mhd structure.

Now we know that the molten layers inside the Earth act just like the cylinder of mercury in Alfven's experiment. As long as they are permeated with mhd energy, they act as if they were plastic, or nearsolid.

We also know that the shell of the Earth - which includes the oceans, the crust, and a teeny part of the mantle - is not dynamically balanced as it stands today. Rough computations show that there is a huge torque of 48.6x10,000,000,000,000,000,000 ton-miles tending to rotate the shell about the Earth's interior; Greenland and Antarctica could move toward the equator in less than half a day were the shell free to make the shift.

As long as the inner mhd energy structure remains strong enough to make the molten layers act as near solids, the shell will not shift its position about the Earth's interior. To be sure, the shell is shifting ever so gradually; the subject is covered excellently in the paper Latitude and Longitude, and the Secular Motion of the Pole by Dr. Markowitz of the U. S. Naval Observatory in Washington, D. C.

However, at the time of a cataclysm the entire Solar System passes through a magnetic null zone in the Milky Way Galaxy. These null zones are sometimes popularly called "reversal zones", and so they are, for the magnetic fields on either side of galactic null zones are in opposite directions. Some physicists have found that we are heading into another null zone at an accelerating rate; it is a known fact of geophysics that the Earth's magnetic field strength, now over 35% less than 300 years ago, is decreasing faster and faster; we are indeed approaching a null zone. In any case, when going through a null zone, our planet's inner mhd energy structure is diminished to the extent that the outer, shallow molten layer, 60 miles thick, is allowed to act as a free liquid. No longer does it bind the shell of the Earth to its interior which starts 120 miles deep, as the mirror was bound through the mercury to the agitator by mhd energy in Hannes Alfven's experiment.

The shell of the Earth is freed to find a new dynamic balance about the Earth's interior. It shifts in the direction the torque imbalance of the shell dictates it must go to find its new balance - and the 60-mile deep, white-hot (2,500+ deg. F.) molten layer beneath the outer solid shell lubricates the shift all the way.

The trigger, then, is our planet's passage (along with the entire Solar System) through a galactic-scale magnetic null zone, diminishing the Earth's inner mhd energy to so low a level that the shallow molten layer, starting at 60 miles deep and extending to 120 miles deep, is allowed to act as a free liquid lubricating layer between the Earth's shell and solid interior.

During each cataclysm the shell finds its new dynamic balance, which is resolved when the shell has shifted to a position with the ice caps rotating equatorially and melting in the heat of the Torrid Zone. As they melt relatively fast, and they usually total around eight million cubic miles of ice (as they do today) , the oceans the world over -after the ice melts - rise about 200 feet with the new-found water.

New polar ice caps form on the areas moved into the polar regions; they will not be centered with our axis of rotation, so a new, growing imbalance is created, to grow as the new ice caps grow, to be resolved when the Earth, with the entire Solar system, passes through another galactic null zone, 10,500 years later.

Regarding the shallow molten layer, some geophysicists and seismologists challenge its existence. In 1924 the great seismologist Beno Gutenberg derived from his earthquake seismographic records that the layer must be there. Since then, Hawaiian seismologists have said "Of course! It's the source of the molten stuff volcanoes spew forth!" and other seismologists say "Well-l-l, it's there but it's not molten, it's plastic, or near solid." They're both right. It's molten, and acts as a near-solid because of its mhd content.

Oceanography gives the answer: IGY data shows that oceanic tides the world over depress the ocean floors three-tenths of the increase in depth of the water between low and high tides. The molten layer has to be beneath the ocean floor for the floor to be pushed into the Earth by just a few feet of water.

As surely as there is life left in the Universe, there is in our Milky Way Galaxy; and as surely there is life in our galaxy, our Solar System will traverse another magnetic null zone in it - indeed many more. This brings us to the subject of the next cataclysm.

As mentioned before, Hale's mathematical analysis sets the Wisconsin era at 14,750 years long. The last cataclysm - Noah or Utnapishtim's flood - would appear to be 6,993 years ago. Adam and Eve's cataclysm - the end of the Laurentian ice age - appears close to 11,543 years ago. Hale's mathematics shows the null zone vs. time structure to be helicoid; and, as the Universe approaches its half-life point, cataclysms occur at an increasing frequency, with shorter era-time periods between them. After the Universe has passed its half-life, cataclysms occur at a decreasing frequency, with time periods between them increasing in a mirror image pattern of the first half-life of the Universe.

It appears that our Universe's half-life was in the middle of the Sudan era, which means that we are in the first of longer eras after the Sudan Basin which embraced the half-life point. Our Arctic era mirrors the Hudson Bay era, which was of 7,000 years duration.

We can now reconstruct the table to show seven eras: four in the past, the present, and two in the future (read from bottom up):

Areas at North Pole (North Polar Eras)	Start (Yrs. to and	End from now)	Duration (Years)
Unknown	+10,507	+25,257	14,750
Bay of Bengal	+7	+10,507	10,500
Arctic Ocean	-6,993	+7	7,000
Sudan Basin	-11,543	-6,993	4,550
Hudson Bay	-18,543	-11,543	7,000
Caspian Sea	-29,043	-18,543	10,500
Wisconsin	-43,793	-29,043	14,750

Of course, there were many eras preceding the Wisconsin era, and there will be an equal number following the Unknown era.

You can see that the dark period of no written history was the Sudan Basin era. Let's look at prehistory from a different viewpoint now - from the standards of our present civilization.

We can see that it takes over 5,000 years just for man to stagger back to his feet through a stone age and forced ignorance. It takes him another 1,000 years to learn to travel intelligently, to begin to overcome superstitions, to establish worthwhile communications, to bury prudery enough to make any significant progress in medicine. The progress of civilization can be measured by the change in man's attitude toward woman in childbirth; read Devils, Drugs, and Doctors by Howard W Haggard, M.D. I can remember when the Obstetrician was considered the lowest of the low in the medical profession. The male inferiority complex is manifested throughout history starting with the Old Testament; in seven centuries of the Inquisition, when 98% of the three million burned at the stake were women; through property rights, inheritance and voting laws; through income inequalities; and through burgeoning rape worldwide. Has he outgrown it yet?

If we look to our technical accomplishments - which have taken us over 6,900 years to achieve - think what we could do if we had 10,500 years. We would be in space as commonly as we walk around the block. Fossil fuels and nuclear energy would belong to the dead past; manmade gravity, which we know how to accomplish right now, and natural magnetism, which we also know how to use right now, would be the means for propulsion, power generation, and communications, as we would have learned the processes of nature sufficiently to duplicate them in controlled fashion for our uses.

It appears from the legends passed on from the Caspian Sea and Wisconsin eras that man did just that with the 10,500 and 14,750 year eras he had. Valmiki writes of vimanas, of the Brahma Weapon and Indra's Dart, of "celestial chariots" and more. Legends of Mu and Atlantis, of great technical achievements as well as moral perversions beyond comparison, spring from the Caspian Sea era. A few legends carry over into the 7,000 year Hudson Bay era, showing some retention of knowledge through the cataclysm of 18,543 years ago.

154

If we look to Nostradamus, we find that his predictions end about year 2,000 A.D. Whether we accept him or not, Edgar Cayce predicts a cataclysm about year 1,999 A.D. Hale's mathematics indicates one to be coming about year 2,000 A.D.

As far as I'm concerned, I'm not satisfied with these figures; to me the cataclysm is due sometime between seven and two hundred years from now. If I had my "druthers" - meaning if the funding were available - I would put the entire subject to an intensive, all-out applied mathematics program to determine as precisely as possible how much time we have before the next cataclysm; then undertake an intensive study to determine what we must do in the time we have left to prepare for it.

Wouldn't you?

CONCLUSION

India

Greece

Egypt

When Indra, King of the Gods, had destroyed the Titan who held the waters of the earth captive in his entrails, he returned to the heights of the Central Mountain with the song of the rains and running waters in his ears. But where his dwelling once stood, he saw only ruins and ashes. So he summoned Visvakarman, god of works and arts, and asked him to build another palace to match his powers. The architect set to work; soon towers, buildings, and gardens rose among lakes and woods. Indra urged him forward impatiently. Each day he called for some fresh marvel, pavilions more richly adorned, statues greater in number and cunning. A fever seemed to burn in him. And Visvakarman, exhausted by his labors, decided to lay a complaint before the Creator of the world. Brahma received him, gave ear, approved, and went to plead his case before Vishnu, the supreme Being. Help was promised.

Soon a young Brahman appeared at the King's palace and demanded audience. Charmed by the light of his eyes, Indra granted his request. "Oh King," said the messenger, "Thy palace shall be the noblest of all." These words were sweet to Indra's ears, and he rejoiced. Vishnu's messenger continued: "It shall be the noblest of palaces which the Indras before thyself sought to build." The King became uneasy. "Dost thou say that there were other Indras, Other Visvakarmans before ourselves, other palaces before mine?" "Indeed yes," the youth answered, "I have seen them."

"Moreover, I have seen the world arise and vanish, arise and vanish again, like a tortoise's shell coming out of Infinite ocean and sinking back. I was present at the dawn and twilight of the Cycles, past counting in their numbers, nor could I count all the Indras and Visvakarmans, even the Vishnus and Brahmas, following one another without end. "

"O Solon, Solon, you Hellenes are but children.... There is no old doctrine handed down among you by ancient tradition nor any science which is hoary with age, and I will tell you the reason behind this. There have been and will be again many destructions of mankind arising out of many causes, the greatest having been brought about by earth-fire and inundation. Whatever happened either in your country or ours or in any other country of which we are informed, any action which is noble and great or in any other way remarkable which has taken place, all that has been inscribed long ago in our temple records, whereas you and other nations did not keep imperishable records. And then, after a period of time, the usual inundation visits like a pestilence and leaves only those of you who are destitute of letters and education. And thus you have to begin all over again as children and know nothing of what happened in ancient times either among us or among yourselves."

As for those genealogies of yours which you have related to us, they are no better than tales of children; for in the first place, you remember one deluge only, whereas there were a number of them. And in the next place there dwelt in your land, which you do not know, the fairest and noblest race of men that ever lived of which you are but a seed or remnant. And this was not known to you

because for many generations the survivors of that destruction made no records."

Plato: Timaeus

(Spoken by a priest of Egypt)

Therefore will not we fear, though the earth be removed, and though the mountains be carried into the midst of the sea;

Though the waters thereof roar and be troubled, though the mountains shake with the swelling thereof.

Psalm 46

THE AUTHOR

Dr. Thomas attended Dartmouth College and Columbia University, graduating from the latter in Electrical Engineering.

As a result of his research and analysis since 1949, Dr. Thomas has become recognized as the world's leading authority in cataclysmology.

His cross-correlation research in the fields of stratigraphy, vertebrate palaeontology, radiology, oceanography, glaciology, seismology, palaeophilology, earth magnetism, anthropology, and other related fields has demonstrated that the cataclysmological concepts as presented by DeLuc in 1779 and Cuvier in 1812 are definitely more acceptable within international scientific circles than they have been previously.

Dr. Thomas' definitive efforts in integrating the various earth sciences have distinguished him as the only American with such a specialized scientific forte.

He devoted twenty years in the writing of The Adam and Eve Story, which included seven years in retranslating Genesis I, II, and III. He is the only person to have formalized the science of cataclysmology, achieved through his first crosscorrelating known, accepted data toward proving or disproving whether cataclysms have happened, then deriving the process of cataclysms, followed by the time schedule of cataclysms, and fifteen years of research in finding their trigger.

Aftermath of the Adam and Eve Story

by

Chan Thomas

To the wolves of the night

Who, on hearing

The winds of the past

Howl into the future

Life is a brief master -

An episode,

A tick of the clock.

There is so little time

To learn from the past

Cataclysms affect us in every conceivable way imaginable. They leave nothing untouched. The years oncoming toward a cataclysm affect us in ways totally different from the years following a cataclysm. So few survive - far less than one percent of all life - that each who survives lives to tell a unique tale, whether survival was by planning and intent or by sheer luck.

I suppose we could call the years leading to a cataclysm the precursor. It is most fitting to devote some time to the precursor; there are definite signs of our traversing into it through the past few years.

In any heretofore presentation on evolution, there has not been one dissertation concerning the effect of cataclysms on evolution. It is apropos that we include at least a short dissertation in this book, since a look at cataclysm-mutation interaction should affect our thinking on many other evolutionary aspects.

Thirdly, there is a lasting historical aspect of the life of Jesus over which prehistoric Mayan, or Naga, has an important influence, and, as you will see, we will be able to correct a long-held misconception we have had. Further, as it is quite apropos, we can review what Jesus had to say about cataclysms.

CONTENTS

What's Happening to Our Magnetic Field

During 1967-68 I was on special assignment with a large aerospace firm on an advanced research project, high in security. While on that project, I found myself conjuring up some questions as to the effect on human physiology when a human is placed in the extreme low-density magnetic fields of outer space - outer meaning beyond the radiation belts - such as astronauts encounter halfway between the Earth and our Moon. On my own time I worked with molecular structure of proteins in the human body, and on the possibility of the low-density magnetic field environment having a carcinogenic (cancer-generating) effect.

It only took me a few weeks, and I arrived at two conclusions: first, the protein structure such as in the muscles and connective tissues would literally come apart after about three months in that environment; and second, in the same duration of time any person in that environment would be subjected to a general malignancy - cancer - from head to toes. I wrote a brief paper on the results of my study and submitted it to my supervisor. It was filed away and ultimately forgotten, and I was informed that it was not within the responsibilities of my task with the company.

In 1968 there was an article on the front page of the Los Angeles Times about two scientists at Hahnemann Medical College who had wondered about the same thing as I - only they decided to find the answer

through experimentation with mice. They put a batchful of mice, all genetically of the same strain, in aluminum cylinders, about six inches or so in diameter, half in a magnetic field environment the same as we live in, and the other half in a magnetic field environment equivalent to being halfway between the Earth and our Moon. Both sets of cylinders had the same physical environment, the same number of male and female mice, the same food, the same lighting, the same play environment, and the same water supply. After three months the mice in the low-density cylinders all suffered the same effects: first, they all simply came apart, all in their protein structure; and second, over 35% suffered visible cancers which could be considered head-to-toes. No analysis was made of internal cancers.

I was so shocked to learn that my conceptual work had been verified by experimental work that I immediately made a telephone call to the two scientists. They were equally shocked to learn of my work, and surprised that I knew why their results had occurred. My supervisor was also shocked at the accuracy of my predictions. The scientists invited me to Hahnemann Medical College to spend a week with them; my company cheerfully paid my traveling expenses.

During my conferences with them in Philadelphia, they told me that there was something which was not released to the press, and was not generally known.

They hoped I could help them with reasons for these results, which disturbed them.

The first thing they told me was that the mice turned criminal in their low-density magnetic field environment.

"Criminal!?" I exclaimed. "How in the dickens do you tell when a mouse turns criminal?" I asked.

"Very simple," was the answer. "There are basic end-cruelties for almost all mammals; mice and humans are no exception.

Cannibalism is the ultimate cruelty, and they turned cannibalistic. Even though they had plenty of the same food as the mice in the normal magnetic field strength cylinders, they indulged in cannibalism as a preference. The mice in the normal cylinders treated each other normally - and ate only their normal food." He paused a moment.

"There's another thing which really confounds us," he continued. "These same mice who turned cannibalistic indulged in forcible rape literally around the clock. That and murder are the other end cruelties."

"Is it possible that you can tell the difference between rape and forcible rape in mice?" I asked. "It seems impossible to differentiate in mice."

"Oh yes," he said, "It happens all the time in the animal world. For instance, sea lions and sea elephants. They use forcible rape commonly. In these mice, almost every act of sexual intercourse in the low-density cylinders was forcible rape, whereas in the normal cylinders, we never saw it. Of course, we must assume it may have happened when we weren't looking."

"Of course, in humans it's easy to differentiate between forcible rape and rape," I offered.

"Legally, it may not be so easy to differentiate," he replied, "but morally I guess it's easy. But what we're interested in here is why they resorted to forcible rape just because of the environment of a low-density magnetic field. We were hoping you could give us at least a concept to go on."

I told him that my work did involve the study of legends concerning civilizations in the years leading to cataclysms, when the Earth's magnetic field was decreasing at an increasing rate as they approached the null zone; and in every instance it appeared that criminality - essentially man's inhumanity to man -appeared to become overwhelming. Even the Navajo Indians spoke of it in their legend of their approach to a cataclysm, but they called it adultery. It's quite possible that their definition of rape in any form, be it forcible or not, was included in the term "adultery".

After all of my study, it seemed strange that it had not entered my mind that rape and forcible rape are a part of the overwhelming criminality in the precursor period preceding a cataclysm. Later, I concluded that it was because I was searching for facts, and it never appeared before me in print. To assume it to be a natural part of the overwhelming criminality, however, seemed to be a proper assumption.

After some consideration, I gave them my conclusion. I would commit that a lowering or lowered magnetic field environment could give its occupants a sense of impending doom. Certainly there would be a feeling that something out of control was destroying them, so why not get what they want irrespective of consequences? In the case of humans, those without empathy turn criminal first. In the case of animals, it is probably proper to assume that there is little or no empathy there to start with.

After my trip home from Philadelphia, I examined statistics from around the world. The

United Nations was reporting huge increases of rape in every nation, regardless of economic status, intellectual level, social mores, governmental status, family structure, plus whether a nation were in either Temperate zone or in the Torrid zone; and regardless of ethnicity or religion or whether a nation had an official state religion. The staggering rise in rape worldwide was a leading factor in the rise of the general crime rate around the world.

In the 1960's and 1970's I was giving speeches on the subject of cataclysmology all over the United States. I remember predicting, after presenting the whole picture, that by 1990 crime would be at such a level in our country that the law enforcement agencies of our nation would not be able to cope with it.

Those of us who are old enough to remember see everyday traffic violations that would have immediately drawn citations now ignored by the police. They are simply too busy. It has gotten so that detectives are so busy that they cannot investigate your case if you are a victim of an attempted murder; they are too busy investigating actual murders. If you are a victim of a hundred thousand or a four hundred thousand-dollar fraud they cannot be bothered with you; they are too busy investigating frauds in the billions of dollars. That includes Attorney Generals and staffs plus District Attorneys and staffs plus the SEC and Federal courts. The crime side includes confidence artists, top executives, bankers, Savings and Loan executives, management personnel, family men, thieves, burglars, addicts, those who sell to addicts, murderers, and almost any level of society, from notables to homeless.

This brings up an extremely important issue. As sure as the Sun rises in the East and sets in the West, the time will come when you must decide whether you and your family should survive the next cataclysm. You will have to decide how to survive over the long term afterward, if you do survive. You must pick a place to survive where survival is possible, the most likely place being on the eastern side of a mountain top which will be accessible when the time comes.

Most important of all, you will have to find a way to protect yourself and your family through the criminally worsening precursor years and the following aftermath years. Surely you will have to have provisions, tools, lumber and supplies with which to build a storm refuge from the cataclysm, clothing, first aid, medical books, binoculars, firewood, means to start a fire, and a library with which to teach the young. Include the Ciba Pharmaceutical volumes by Frank Netter, M.D. Further, include my book, Natural Childbirth Self-Taught - the only book written on the subject, and I have been teaching Natural Childbirth for 43 years.

In the preceding paragraph, I started by saying Most important of all, etc. How will you protect your family against attack when the police can't? How will you protect your wife and daughters against gang rape and murder if the marauding gangs pay you a sudden visit? Those who have not prepared for a cataclysm far outnumber those who have. Those who have not will want what you have, and will kill you to get it. Both shortly before and after the cataclysm. You will be besieged by those begging you to share your provisions.

They will appear to be nice families, wanting to share, wanting to help, and wanting what you have. Believe me, they will kill you to get it. If you look at history, let alone prehistory, when those who have have no protection, the have nots will kill the haves to get what the haves have. And they will destroy it to get it.

Are you ready to make an instantaneous decision to protect yourself and family? A decision which will make the lives and safety of yourself and your family inexorable? If you wait to see if your "visitors" have evil intent so that afterward you can take protective action, you and your family will wind up murdered, raped, and dead. And history dictates that you will be tortured just as a means of supplying your "visitors" with pleasure.

Survival is not a nice or easy picture to paint when all of the forces intended to protect and defend you have completely vanished. If you live at the time of a cataclysm, and have the time to prepare for it, you will have to assume attitudes and perspectives, principles and actions, and willingness to act, in multifaceted ways you never dreamed you would in order to survive. You will have to abide by the law until there is no law, then survive by the rules necessary to make survival possible under all potential onslaughts.

How do you know when it is time for a cataclysm? The answer is simple. Go to a store soon where you can

purchase a top-quality magnetic compass, one wherein you can lock the free north-south indicating needle in any position you desire.

The bigger it is, the better off you are. Then purchase an accurate stopwatch.

Take them home and put them by your bedside. Have a paper under the compass with two diameters marked off at 90 degrees to each other in a circle larger than the diameter of your compass. Put your compass on the paper, centered within the circle. Unlock the compass needle and set it on north. Set the compass case so that its north coincides with the compass needle, and place the paper underneath so that one of its diameters is on the north-south line of the compass needle and the compass case. Tape the paper in place. Put the compass back so that its needle is pointed north, along the north-south line on the paper underneath. Then to bed and have a good night's sleep.

In the morning, hold the compass steadily as it is positioned in the circle beneath it, and lock the needle in place. Then turn the compass case left or right 90 degrees; use the 90-degree line on the paper underneath as a guide. Hold the case absolutely still, then release the needle. The needle will then swing toward north, and oscillate back and forth, diminishing in its swing a little each time. With the stopwatch, observe the time the time necessary for the compass needle to stop oscillating from its release time to first quiet settled-down time.

There will come the day, if indeed we are going to enter the galaxy's magnetic null zone as soon as the mathematics tables indicate we will, that you will find the settling down time increasing, as the needle's oscillations will become sluggish. It could be that the time for settling down will stay nearly the same, but the number of oscillations required for the needle to settle down will decrease. So, perhaps in addition to recording the stopwatch time duration, also record the number of oscillations required for the needle to settle down. Either way, you will discern by your data that indeed, the Earth's magnetic field strength has decreased to a critical level. NOW! Take your family and your entire survival storage to your retreat. I hope you will not have waited this long to pack it and get it ready to go. Leave behind everything you can do without. Be sure to take with you whatever instruments (and the supplies for those instruments) needed for your protection and survival. Be sure your family is well trained in their use.

There is a mathematical law that any predictions based on extending existing data are subject to the possibility of a fifth degree error. That means that any prediction for the time of the next cataclysm is subject to that error, and nothing can be done about it. Do you know that the law applies equally to the President's and House of Representative's and the Senate's ability to form an annual federal budget? They can't fix a budget and stick to it. The best they can do is guess-estimate.

In the case of the magnetic compass, it experimentally establishes a known data point each day, so you will always know within a day whenever your prediction should be. If 2,000 A.D. passes by without a cataclysm, the best thing for you to do is to stick with it and maintain your vigil. When the day does come, you will be happy to have advance notice, as short or long as it might be. It was found that in Tiahuanaco the populace was caught entirely offguard, with people doing what they normally do; everyone was caught, completely surprised, in the unbelievable magnitude and suddenness of the maelstrom of a cataclysm's precipitous onslaught.

If you choose to go all-out with your survival preparation, do decide to indulge in some heavy work in pouring concrete - with walls and ceiling up to four feet thick, with extremely heavy steel reinforcing, on the eastern side of the peak of a top-high mountain.

If you can, pick two, three, or four families who will share your survival desires with you to the extent that they will work with you in preparing for survival of the cataclysm. Be sure to have families who can get along together extremely well; have good, strong teenage children who can be friends; have record-keeping capabilities to keep records of marriages, births and deaths. Have family trees for records also. At least one father should be ordained non-denominationally. And BE SURE no one's a drinker, smoker or narcotic user.

Bear it in mind that the odds for survival are mighty, mighty low. They're lower than winning the Publishers Clearing House's ten million dollars. Of course, those odds include the millions upon millions of persons who think the whole concept of cataclysms is a bunch of rot and don't even try to prepare for survival. Perhaps the best way to look at the odds for survival is to look at how many survive out of those who really prepare for survival. We can't even estimate that, for who knows from past experience? It all depends upon the best efforts possible in planning and preparing for the cataclysm and postcataclysm - structurally, energywise, toolwise, medically, spiritually, travelwise, maintenancewise, securitywise, communications wise, food supply-wise, and don't forget the can opener.

What to take to read is vitally important. What tools are necessary to take is of ultimate importance.

If you do not survive, do remember that death is but a steppingstone. Everyone goes through its portals. Further, what a way to go! How many humans ever get to see a cataclysm?

And after you go through those portals, there is a peace that defies description, that passeth all understanding.

I wouldn't be surprised if I see you there. And further, I wouldn't be surprised if we have a nice talk.

EVOLUTION

If ever there were a controversy in the world of science, it is in the subject of evolution. Even the name creates angry reaction in some scientists when it is called The Theory of Evolution.

In each and every field of science, there is a strong standard of procedure known as The Scientific Process. It is the one standard procedure common to all sciences wherein research is necessary to establish a scientific law. These stages constitute a scientific order of procedure utilized to establish that scientific law.

Let's take a totally unrelated field to that of this book as an example: ESP, or Extra-Sensory Perception. For years scientists evaded this field of research in fear of besmirching their scientific escutcheons. Others took up the cudgel, expending years of effort in experimental research, trying to prove or disprove whether such a phenomenon exists. Not one of them formed a hypothesis to try to lay down how it works, if it works. All they did was to formulate tests to be performed to indicate that the phenomenon did or did not exist. That a hypothesis does not make. Forming a hypothesis is the first step in The Scientific Process.

I put together a hypothesis, formulating how the communication system works, utilizing the known forces of nature, plus a means for testing the hypothesis to determine whether it was valid.

It worked with everyone on whom we tried the test, man, woman, adult and child; and I'm speaking of quantitative testing here, with one hundred percent success in every case.

The Scientific Process requires progressing front hypothesis to theory to law. Having proven my hypothesis, that meant that there now existed a valid theory concerning ESP. The next step to determine whether the theory is a law was to determine the predictability of ESP based on testing the theory as to its predictability. This is an extremely difficult factor to test in the field of human experience, because human events are not immutable. If you feel that an event is going to happen to you which you do not want to happen, you can change circumstances to prevent its happening. Then how could you prove that it would have happened if you had not changed circumstances? If you had not changed circumstances and it did happen, how could you prove that you knew it was going to happen? Predictability was extremely difficult as a test.

I won't go into the complex details, but we were able to prove predictability under controlled circumstances. That meant that we definitely had a firm law on our hands. I took that law and formulated a course that could be taught; UCLA welcomed my course into their

Experimental College, where I taught it to 140 students with extreme success for four quarters.

Those 140 students were 140 new students each quarter for four quarters, making it 560 students I had taught. I entered this task with the haunting doubt it my mind as to whether I could teach students how to perform ESP in large groups, even in subgroups doing their own testing in twenty groups of seven each. I was amazed to find that there was no communication interference between groups; each group was independently performing its own communications. It was a further test of predictability, even though I had serious doubts as to whether it would succeed. I had previously taught ESP, only one-on-one. The law was strengthened. By the way, the course was very popular with a long waiting list, I was told by the administrator.

By all scientific measurements, the "Theory of Evolution" is but a rank, raw hypothesis, based on two counts. Let's look at those counts.

First, it is assumed that evolution of the species is a gradual process of improvement. If so, why do we see as universal the gradual degradation of the species? Why does performance of the pancreas diminish on a percentage basis as the years go by? Why has diabetes become so prevalent in just three to four generations? Why have intelligence levels lowered so markedly? Why has the percentage of students not wanting to learn increased so markedly? Why has crime increased and empathy decreased so markedly? Is that improvement?

Why has teeth structure so deteriorated in so many places of the world? Why is it that so few have a natural resistance to tooth decay? Why is it that so many have no resistance to tooth decay? The military, in scientific curiosity, established a research program involving those in the military who had absolute resistance to tooth decay. There were not many who qualified to participate in the program. Why? Nobody knows. Those running the tests and analyses never did find out how and why those who were immune were immune.

Gradual improvement of the species cannot be measured by bone structure alone, combined with assumptions. We're surrounded by gradual degradation.

The second point is that nowhere do we find any analysis of evolution by mutation. Mutation is a sudden change, usually from one generation to the next, sometimes extensive change sufficient to completely hide the preceding generation; sometimes small enough to allow a reasonable analysis. Let's look at how this comes about.

During a cataclysm, the turbulence surrounding our planet is sufficient to completely disrupt the high altitudes' structure which shields the Earth from the deadly cosmic rays.

Very few cosmic rays normally penetrate that shield. During a cataclysm, when the shield is totally broken up, cosmic rays gain complete access to the Earth, bombarding it in plethora. Of the very, very few who survive, some have been struck by cosmic rays; some have not. It is impossible to determine the ratio.

Georges Cuvier was the first to study fossil bones in light of the environment in which they were found. Some were found in one sedimentary strata; some in another; and some in another, and so on and so on. He was also the discoverer of the relative structure of bones of different species, and the definition of an entire skeleton based on comparative anatomy which he himself had discovered and established. What a pioneer! He could be given a piece of a bone, or a tooth, and tell you exactly which species it belonged to.

Cuvier noted that the species found in one strata seemed to be totally wiped out, suddenly, by the deposit of the strata in which they were found, and the next upper strata would contain new species with no antecedents whatsoever.

Without realizing it, he had discovered the mutations of species caused by cataclysms. Those species - including humans - which and who had had their gonads bombarded by cosmic rays, had a genetic change wrought in the sperms or eggs they were carrying, and/or in the parent cells in their gonads. Consequently, a random result occurred: their offspring varied randomly in the degree of mutation, but nevertheless mutation was universal in the offspring of parents, one or both of whom had had their eggs and/or sperms bombarded by cosmic rays. The offspring resulting from mutated parent cells was and is totally unpredictable.

If we utilize the modern mathematical science of applied mathematics, it tells us that it is impossible to have upgrading species through mutation. It is equally impossible to have an even crossover in quality from normal parents to mutated offspring. The sure bet is that mutational offspring represent the most sudden degradation of the genes to varying, random degrees.

If we again use applied mathematics, that science tells us that it is utterly impossible that the human being is a result of millions, perhaps billions of years of upgrading evolution from a single cell. It has to be that the human being is a result of a design and resulting productions of two variations of that design: male and female.

You can name any source as the creator of that design and producer of the first models, male and female. If you were to ask me, I could tell you the exact steps which had to be undertaken to produce the living products. I could tell you how the design produced both male and female - a product of sheer genius. Do you know that we are that close to being able to create male and female ourselves? Someday I'll probably be writing and making speeches about it.

Previously: "nowhere do we find any analysis of evolution by mutation." This is not exact.

Anthropologists are now finding that certain species of birds are descendants of dinosaurs. If true, it is a startling revelation of the veracity of mutational descendance, as that relationship could not have been through gradual evolution, be it upgrading (which is impossible) or downgrading.

Proof that man (and woman) are the closest we have to the original design after untold thousands of years of cataclysms and mutations is through his abstract functions, plus a few concrete functions. Speech and the capability of learning and maintaining an extensive vocabulary are good examples of concrete functions. Abstract functions include three-dimensional visualization, inductive reasoning, deductive reasoning, and analytical reasoning. And of course we must include empathy. Even some species of humans are totally lacking in empathy. In any case, humans have unique and more complete brains than any other species.

Remember that, especially in the years preceding and following a cataclysm, those without empathy turn criminal first. If there is any doubt in your mind about that, just read the newspapers. Watch TV news. Watch TV crime documentary programs. Think it over. Then draw your own conclusions.

JESUS AS HISTORY

There are three passages in the Bible which concern us from the viewpoint of history alone. They are in the New Testament: (1) Matthew 27:34 and 45 thru 50; (2) Mark 15:33 thru 37; (3) John 19:28 thru 30.

(1) "34 They gave him vinegar to drink mingled with gall: and when he had tasted thereof, he would not drink.

45 Now from the sixth hour there was darkness over all the land unto the ninth hour.

46 And about the ninth hour Jesus cried with a loud voice, saying, Eli, Eli, la-ma sa-bach-tha-ni? that is to say, My God, my God, why hast thou forsaken me?

47 Some of them that stood there, when they heard that, said, This man calleth for E-li-as.

48 And straightway one of them ran, and took a sponge, and filled it with vinegar, and put it on a reed, and gave him to drink.

49 The rest said, Let be, let us see whether E-li-as will come to save him.

50 Jesus, when he had cried again with a loud voice, yielded up the ghost."

(2) "33 And when the sixth hour was come, there was darkness over the whole land until the ninth hour.

34 And at the ninth hour Jesus cried with a loud voice, ^{sa}ying, E-lo-i, Eloi, la-ma sa-hach-tha-ni? which, is bei^{n}g interpreted, My God, my God, why hast thou forsaken me?

35 And some of them that stood by, when they said, Behold, he calleth E-li-as.

36 And o^{ne} ^{ran} and filled a sponge full of vinegar,

and put it on a reed, saying, Let alone; let us see

whether E-li-as will come to take him down.

37 And Jesus cried with a loud voice, and gave up the ghost."

(3)

"28 After this, Jesus knowing that all things were

now accomplished, that the scripture might be fulfilled,

saith, I thirst.

29 Now there was set a vessel full of vinegar: and

they filled a sponge with vinegar, and put it upon

hyssop, and put it to his mouth.

30 When Jesus therefore had received the vinegar,

he said, It is finished: and he bowed his head, and gave up the ghost."

Luke had a totally different view of the sequence of events. He didn't even record whether Jesus said he was thirsty, as John did; he didn't record the words Jesus spoke as Matthew and Mark did. Starting with the verse where he did agree with the others, let's look at Luke 24: 44 through 46:

"44 And it was about the sixth hour, and there was a darkness over all the earth until the ninth hour.

45 And the sun was darkened, and the veil of the temple was rent in the midst.

46 And when Jesus had cried with a loud voice, he said, Father, into thy hands I commend my spirit: and having said thus, he gave up the ghost."

You can see that Luke omitted the scene where Jesus spoke the words Matthew and Mark quoted and interpreted, and which many in the crowd thought were Jesus saying he was thirsty, and of which John thought so little of it that he merely quoted Jesus as saying "I thirst." Luke also omitted the action, after Jesus' strange words, of someone, thinking Jesus was thirsty, putting vinegar on a sponge, then putting the sponge on a reed, and giving the vinegar to Jesus. Matthew, Mark and John related this sponge and vinegar scene, which Luke omitted completely. It would seem that we should pass by Luke as a credible witness.

Now let's discuss those words which Jesus spoke, so vividly described by Matthew and Mark.

"Eli, Eli, la-ma sa-bach-tha-ni" and

"Eloi, Eloi, la-ma sa-bach-tha-ni".

Both Matthew and Mark put a question mark after their quote of Jesus' words.

When Jesus spoke them, he created quite a bit of confusion. Some said, "Hey, he's calling Elias." (Maybe he'll come and save him!) Others said that he was thirsty. John said simply, "Jesus said, I thirst."

Someone in the crowd, thinking Jesus had said he was thirsty, soaked a sponge in vinegar, put it on a reed and held it to Jesus' mouth.

We must give immense credit to Matthew and Mark for writing down as best as they could the sounds of the words Jesus spoke. From what they wrote, we know that no such words existed in Hebrew at that time. Nor did they exist in Aramaic nor in Greek nor in any other language of which we know for that area and that time.

Why did Jesus, in his dying moments, use a language which no one else knew? The best Matthew and Mark could do was say "which is, being interpreted" and "that is to say". Thank God for their honesty.

As for the difference between Matthew's "Eli, Eli" and Mark's "Eloi, Eloi" we must consider the crowd's reaction. The only reaction quoted is in both Matthew and Mark as Jesus having said "Elias". If we are reduced to a choice, we would have to go along with "Eli, Eli."

I searched and searched, and could not find the words in any language either. In desperation I turned to the parent language, Prehistoric Mayan or Naga.

There the words were, as large as life:

Heli, heli, lamat sabac ta ni.

I am fainting, I am fainting, darkness is overcoming me.

Since Jesus is quoted as having "cried with a loud voice" in both Matthew and Mark, perhaps we should quote the translation to be:

I am fainting! I am fainting!

Darkness is overcoming me!

This opens up a bucketful of questions and controversies. Imagine what I was faced with as soon as I found the translation. I was faced with a mountain to climb. If I didn't climb it, I would never sleep again. I knew that, like solving the puzzles of cataclysmology, this problem would never leave me alone - mainly for the sake of my own and my Dear Wife's curiosity.

A hundred questions crossed my mind. Well, maybe not a hundred. But a plethora of them, anyway.

Why did Jesus, in his dying moments, speak a language which no one whom we know of heard him speak before? Was he naturally reverting to a language he had spoken as a prime language in earlier years?

If so, where had he been to have picked up that language? And used it habitually?

Let's again look to the Bible as history. A good place to start is Luke 2: 41, where Jesus' parents are mentioned:

"41 Now his parents went to Jerusalem every year at the feast of the passover.

42 And when he was twelve years old, they went up to Jerusalem after the custom of the feast.

43 And when they had fulfilled the days, as they returned, the child Jesus tarried behind in Jerusalem; and Joseph and his mother knew not of it.

44 But they, supposing him to have been in the company, went a day's journey; and they sought him among their kinfolk and acquaintance.

45 And when they found him not, they turned back again to Jerusalem, seeking him.

46 And it came to pass, that after three days they found him in the temple, sitting in the

midst of the doctors, both hearing them, and asking them questions.

47 And all that heard him were astonished at his understanding and answers.

48 And when they saw him, they were amazed: and his mother said unto him, Son, why hast thou thus dealt with us? behold, thy father and I have sought thee sorrowing.

49 And he said unto them, How is it that ye sought me? wist ye not that I must be about my Father's business?"

This one story tells us that Jesus had to be a genius of his day. Also, it tells us that he had an affinity for dropping in at the temple to share minds with the adult intelligentsia on an equal plane.

One more fact should be taken into account in our summation of contributing factors, and that is that there is a total of only fifty-five days of Jesus' life accounted for in the Bible. We are left with him at age 12 in the incident above, and brought back into his life when he is about thirty (Luke 3: 23).

This leaves about eighteen years of Jesus' life unaccounted for in the Bible. Is there any other source?

In the mid-1800's, the British Army was stationed in northern India, near the town of Ahoydia, prehistorically known as Adjudia. They discovered that there was a temple there, of which there were only three of that kind in India. In pre-Brahman India, all temples were of this kind, and were called Nacaal Temples. The official language of these temples, the British found out, was Naga, or Prehistoric Mayan.

Curiously enough, there was a tribe in the extreme north of India, called the Naga tribe. This tribe, even today, speaks pure Naga as their everyday language. They told the British of Jesus' having been there as a late-teenager-young-adult who attended the Nacaal Temple as a student and graduate of the Temple.

He was especially remembered through tradition because he was a genius. Students were taught rigorous courses, from mathematics to medicine, languages, what we call ESP, out-of-body travel, metaphysics as a science, and natural healing. The course was so rigorous that it usually took the lifetime of a normal person to graduate from the temple. Students had to learn Naga.

Graduates were called Son of God. It's interesting that Jesus never referred to himself as Son of God, but always Son of man.

The Nagas' tale of Jesus includes Jesus' becoming a student as a young man, and through his genius he went through the courses in record time as a student, Master and Graduate at 25 to 30 years old.

On investigating, I found that travel was quite common between the Holy Land and India in Jesus' time. He could have made the trip there very easily at fifteen to twenty and back just as easily ten to fifteen years later.

We are also informed of Jesus' proclivity for dropping into temples just to have intellectual and spiritual discourse with adult intelligentsia.

Imagine his going to India, happening onto the Nacaal Temple, dropping in for some discourse, and afterward deciding that there was the place for him to stay and really learn.

Spending ten to fifteen years learning to speak and write Naga, and speaking it as his sole language for that duration, certainly would account for his reverting to it on the cross as his natural language.

There is another point in question which has to do with doctrine taught at the Temple. The entire philosophy of religion as Jesus taught it was exactly as he had learned it at the Temple. Never would he have entertained the thought that God would or might forsake him, under any circumstances whatsoever, on or off of the cross, or anywhere. Only humans would.

At this point we should summarize everything we can about the events surrounding the moments when Jesus spoke those words on the cross, and apply whatever reasoning we can in order to cover every aspect involved toward either verifying or refuting our translation of his words.

First: Our only reasonable source of the words Jesus actually spoke is through Matthew and Mark.

Second: It is abundantly clear that Jesus spoke in a loud voice. There is a difference between listening to sounds and hearing them; Matthew and Mark listened to him to the extent that they were able to write down the phonetics of what Jesus said to the best of their ability. We should recognize that their attention to the details of the phonetics was enhanced by the loudness with which Jesus spoke. John didn't pay much attention to detail; he just heard Jesus speak loudly, and assumed that Jesus said merely, "I thirst" without even attempting to listen to or write down the phonetics of the words Jesus spoke.

Third: Our only primary source of the meaning of those words is through Matthew, Mark, and John. Matthew said, "That is to say,....";

Mark said, "....which is, being interpreted,...."; and John said,

"Jesus....saith, I thirst." It is clear that Matthew and Mark were not

translating, but giving us their best guesses what the words Jesus spoke meant. John just guessed outright.

The most interesting aspect of Matthew's and Mark's recordings is that the phonetics of Jesus' words and their meaning are so nearly alike - with one syllable, "li" as recorded by Matthew, and "loi" as recorded by Mark being the only difference. It appears that each had his own memory (as referred to by those in the field of aptitude studies as "Tonal Memory") of the sounds of the syllable, suggesting independent recording of the phonetics by each of them. However, their interpretations of the meaning of Jesus' words are precisely the same, suggesting that they conferred with each other, comparing their interpretations, and arriving at a mutually agreed upon interpretation of what Jesus meant by what he spoke loudly. Certainly neither of them compared their memories with Luke or John. It appears that we must honor Matthew's and Mark's accuracy in recording the sounds of the words Jesus spoke. It's plausible, since Jesus spoke loudly.

Fourth: We have no secondary source of the words Jesus spoke; we only have secondary sources through Matthew, Mark, and John, who tell us about the crowd at the scene and their reaction to what they thought Jesus said. Some in the crowd said, "Hey, he's calling Elias! Maybe he'll come and get him down off the cross!" - As if it were a big joke. Some others said, "He says he's thirsty! Someone give him a drink!" So someone ran to a bowl of vinegar, put a sponge on a reed, soaked it in the vinegar and held it to Jesus' lips.

Of course, John added his bit by writing "Jesus saith, I thirst."

It is obvious that there was a great amount of confusion resulting from Jesus' words, with three known interpretations of those words. Isn't it interesting and provocative that those three versions differed from each other to the extent that there is absolutely no comparison between them?

Fifth: It is a fact that Jesus' words did not exist in any known language at that time, including Hebrew, Aramaic, and Greek. "Eli" expressly was not a part of the Hebrew tongue; it was entered into that language since then to mean "My God". It seems strange that those who fostered and shouted for his crucifixion would be the ones to adopt one of the words Jesus spoke on the cross into their language.

Sixth: We must take into consideration Jesus' physical condition at the time he spoke those strange words.

Contra to one of the popular myths, Jesus was nor nailed to the cross through his hands and spaces through his bones in his lower feet leading to his toes. It was a common form of execution in that time, and always, the nails were driven through a space in the wrist bones as, if driven through the hands, the crucified could pull his hands off of the nails easily while on the cross. Plus, the same conditions existed in the feet of the crucified: in order to keep him from pulling his feet off of the nails, the nail or nails had to be driven through a space between the upper foot bones. Therefore, the crucified became literally a prisoner of the cross. The only way to get him off of the cross was to pull the nails.

The crucified was nailed to the cross in such a way that, with his knees bent somewhat, he could hang by his arms and rest his legs. After a while his diaphragm would enter the early stages of paralysis, and he would feel suffocation oncoming. Then he would straighten his legs, standing on his nailed feet, providing relief for his arms from bearing the stress of holding up his body, thereby relieving the stress on his diaphragm leading to paralysis and suffocation. Consequently, he endured a running continuum of up and down, up and down, up and down for hours and hours.

Those responsible for performing the crucifixion had a way of stopping this endurance test. They simply broke the legs of the crucified so that he couldn't stand on them anymore. He was forced to hang by his arms without surcease; he soon fell into full paralysis of his diaphragm and died of suffocation.

It is known that Jesus suffered "scourging" for some time before his walk to crucifixion with Simon of Cyrene, who was compelled by soldiers to carry his cross. "Scourging" meant torture with whips with barbs in the ends of the lashes of each whip; those barbs ate deeply through Jesus' skin and into his flesh. It had to be excruciatingly painful. While on his walk to Golgotha, Jesus was still sufficiently conscious to have made the walk successfully; he had not yet entered a state of deep shock.

There were three men crucified at the same time on Golgotha. Jesus, of course, was in the middle. The other two had not been tortured before their crucifixion.

After they were on their crosses, Jesus entered into deep shock. In that condition it was impossible for him to feel any pain. While in that condition, he lost consciousness; and while entering that state, he said loudly (as quoted by Matthew):"Eli, Eli, la-ma-sa-bach-tha-ni?".

It has been popularly assumed that pain drove Jesus to say those words. Impossible. He was feeling no pain. He was in deep shock, on the verge of passing out. It is most logical that he was saying 'I am fainting, I am fainting, darkness is overcoming me!". It is most illogical that Jesus would be complaining in a loud voice that God had forsaken him. As I said before, he knew absolutely that only humans would do that.

This is an apropos time to consider The Shroud of Turin. The image on - or in - it shows the barb gouges of a whipping scourging, plus showing that the legs of the victim were not broken - as Jesus' were not.

Further, the image shows irrefutable signs that the victim had been crowned with a crown of thorns, as Jesus had been.

Further still, the image shows irrefutable signs of the victim having been crucified in the standard manner.

Those parts of the image - the proof of barbed whipping scourging; the proof of the victim being crucified; the unbroken legs, which was most unusual in a crucifixion; and the crown of thorns worn by the victim - all point to Jesus as being the wearer of that controversial shroud.

The crown of thorns is the most powerful indicator of Jesus being the wearer. Who else but Jesus would have been so crowned as a part of his scourging, scourging itself being almost never employed? And crowned for whatever reason, in Jesus' case for derision as "King of the Jews"?

There is a last subject to consider: how the image was made on the Shroud of Turin. This is a point of great controversy among scientists.

How it was accomplished is known only to those of us who have found how Nature makes gravity.

ANGELS and UFOs

Now we come to a disputant subject. If you stick your toe in the water, it either gets burned or frozen. It could create a controversy in a millisecond. Or maybe even a microsecond.

In one aspect I have a distinct advantage, for I know how Nature makes gravity. Once we understand the process, the procedure for us to produce manmade gravity is to duplicate Nature's process in controlled fashion. Once we understand this, we can expand our understanding to include propulsion, communications, and weaponry. Any nation, large or small, which finds this process will have the world at its mercy. Any nation which discovers how to use it for any one of the three purposes automatically has the other two.

Any nation - even the smallest - having all three processes will control our planet with unchallengeable invincibility.

Also, we can understand just about every UFO sighting and experience, how and why small UFOs are built as they are, and why large UFOs are easier to design and construct just from considerations of the power plant; of course, a fifty-mile long mother ship would be more difficult to manufacture if we consider structural requirements. I have seen several of these behemoths, along with many other persons. I have seen the smaller, "discus"-like vehicles also. Note that a common cross-section of all of these vehicles, behemoth and small, is to have just one cross-section circular.

Now we come to another factor. What is an angel? And further, who is an angel? Matthew, Mark, Luke and John wrote about angels as if they were a normal, accepted part of life in their times.

It all started when Mary Magdalene, Mary the mother of James, and Salome decided to go to the sepulchre where Jesus was buried. There they found the blocking stone removed, and

Jesus gone. They found one or two men there; Matthew said he was an angel, whose "countenance was like lightning, and his raiment white as snow". Mark said, "And entering into the sepulchre, they saw a young man sitting on the right side, clothed in a long white garment....". Not once did Mark mention that there was an angel there. Luke said, "And it came to pass, as they (presumably the three women) were much perplexed thereabout, behold, two men stood by them in shining garments:". John said, "But Mary....stooped down and looked into the sepulchre, and seeth two angels in white sitting, the one at the head, and the other at the feet, where the body of Jesus had lain."

There is an entertaining game which sometimes is played at parties. Everyone sits in chairs in a circle, and the first on one end is given a short message in writing. Each person relays the message verbally, whispering the message into the next person's ear until the last person in the circle receives it and writes it down.

Invariably the two written messages bear little resemblance to each other. If we go through the circle, each one telling what the message was that he received, we find that the message deteriorated each time it was relayed. Sometimes one step in the relaying circle changes the whole meaning of the message. Try it some time when you're at a party. It's fun and revealing.

The strange thing is that the mathematics of communications theory, an exact science, predicts this deterioration in relaying intelligent information; the more links in the relay, the more the deterioration. The worst series of links is to have all of the links human, like the ring of chairs, one person per chair. The more persons, the more ridiculous the deterioration.

Now none of Matthew, Mark, Luke and John were at the sepulchre, so what they wrote was

228

not firsthand information. Even if each one of them had spoken to the same woman of the three who went to the sepulchre, her story could or would have differed each time she told it to one of the four. Or, if each of the women told the story to a different disciple, the story most certainly would have varied. Further, if none of them told the disciples the story, but the disciples were told the story by a mix of secondary sources, it would have varied greatly. The fact is that we don't know how Matthew, Mark, Luke and John got the sepulchre story. That can't be changed.

In spite of all of the differences between the four relatings of the same story, we have to take into account each version, if nothing more than just to see where we stand.

Matthew stated: One angel; countenance like lightning; raiment white as snow; the angel spoke to the women; all had fear of the angel.

Mark stated: One young man, seated on right side; clothed in a long white garment; the three women were "affrighted"; he spoke to the women.

Luke stated: Two men in shining garments were standing by the women; the women were afraid; both spoke to the women, saying the same words.

John stated: Mary Magdalene alone stood outside the sepulchre; stooping and looking in, she saw two angels in white; angels were sitting one at the head, one at the feet, where Jesus had lain. They conversed with her; no fear was mentioned. She saw Jesus, and did not recognize him; she thought he was the gardener.

John's relation varies so much from the other three that it suggests a different event. It appears that she visited the sepulchre with the other women, then ran back, encountered Peter, and told him that the stone was taken away from the sepulchre; the two of them then ran back to the sepulchre to start this story.

So what can we conclude from these four stories? Let's see.

1. The angels looked like men; in fact, they must have been men.

2. Whether there were one or two of them, he or they wore long, bright white, clean, glistening robes.

3. Although strangers, they could speak Hebrew, and spoke calmly and authoritatively to the women.

4. Whether one or two of them, they had countenances which caused fear in the women, except in the story related by John. It could be that Mary Magdalene, in her first visit to the sepulchre with the other two women, had visited with the man or men at that time, and who had dispelled the women's fears with his or

their words, so when she returned, she had no fear.

What about these men? They were not known anywhere; they were dressed totally differently than anyone in the area, or even far away from that area; they showed absolutely no fear of anyone or anything; and Matthew stated that the angel of the Lord descended from heaven and rolled back the stone from the door (of the sepulchre). I'll bet a pound of earth that he was waiting at the sepulchre for those who crucified Jesus to show up, hence his countenance was like lightning.

It looks as if we must conclude that these men, these angels, came to Earth in their space vehicle to take care of the aftermath of Jesus' crucifixion. Let's say that their space vehicle was an Ezekiel's wheel. Any dissenter's only alternative to this is name-calling.

So why would these men, these angels, watch over Jesus? The only answer is in legend, in that they watched over him because he was a genius, a man who had graduated from the Nacaal temple in so short a time that he could spend his life taking his learnings of the true faith from the temple, turn them into teachings, taking them to the rest of the world.

These people from other worlds never come here to live because this planet is the garbage dump of the Universe. We murder, rape, steal, wage war - killing millions; there are millions of young girls and women of the Eastern hemisphere sexually mutilated to prevent them from having sexual intercourse before marriage; there is forced prostitution by kidnapping, child females being sold into marriage, then sold into prostitution; out and out slavery; greed beyond comparison; wanton destruction of our planet by pollution and greed; unbridled reproduction without responsibility; the spread of deathdealing disease by irresponsible action; all of these deeds being perpetrated as commonly as you and I sprinkle salt on food. On top of this, we have a worldwide addiction to narcotics and narco-selling.

We have wife-beating, girlfriend-beating, childbeating, and murder on an unprecedented scale in our country; so prevalent in other countries that it is a matter of normalcy. Rape is so common the world over that if we were to stop it, knowing where and how to stop it would be as difficult as knowing where and how to stop narcotics abuse and selling which has the world firmly by the tail now.

Governments have deteriorated to a point where our whole planet is near anarchy. Some governments are on the brink of wipeout from losses to AIDS.

Let's just take a look at our government, the Federal government of the U.S.A. Do you know that every government official who approves of the federal budget violates his oath to preserve, protect and defend the Constitution of the United States of America?

Consequently, each one who approves a federal budget every year is subject to impeachment? Why is each one approving a federal budget not impeached? Because there are too many of them?

Probably. Why should each one approving a budget be impeached? Let's see.

Our government is in business, in fact over 4,000 businesses. Each and every one of them loses money every year. They make up for their losses every year by asking the legislature to appropriate funds to cover their losses. The legislature appropriates those funds.

How our government ever got into over 4,000 businesses to begin with is a question for historians to answer; I won't attempt to analyze it here. The point is, we are in these businesses, how legal is it for our government to be in any business, and what can be done about it?

It has always been an axiom of Constitutional law that if it's not in the Constitution, the Government cannot do it.

Perhaps you may remember the occasion during the last months of President Reagan's administration, he was invited to an assembly of seniors of three high schools in Florida to address them. In the question and answer period afterward, the valedictorian of each class was allowed to ask a question. When the last one, a girl, rose for her question, the President was being rushed off the stage by his aides. He told her to go ahead with her question while he was walking to the side and rear of the stage. She asked, "What can Congress do?" The President, reaching the right rear corner of the stage with his arm upraised, shouted back, "If it's not in the Constitution, they can't do it!" and then he was gone. In law, he was right; in practice, he was dead wrong. Congress and the President have been violating that point of law for years.

If anyone in any branch of the U.S. Government grants approval of funds for any business in which the government is engaged, he or she is approving the government's participation in an unconstitutional activity which is not authorized by the Constitution of the U.S.A, and is therefore breaking his or her oath of office to preserve, protect and defend the Constitution of the United States of America. The same goes for any executive, President included, who signs the appropriation of funds or dispenses them.

Do you know how much the annual taps on the treasury by those government business losses cost us? The total of all personal income taxes, estate taxes, and gift taxes. And those businesses, all of them, pay no taxes, and pay no rent.

Further, in the history of estate taxes and gift taxes, our government has never netted a dime. They spend all they collect collecting it. Congress has to borrow for that part of the business losses to make up for the non-netting estate and gift taxes.

IRS has an estate tax audit rate of 105% to 110% annually. Why can't they trust themselves?

Our government lies to its citizenry as policy. Consider how much they have lied to the U.S. about MIA's in Vietnam. When Congress and the President passed the excise tax law during WWII, they promised that the law was merely to raise wartime funds, and that the tax would be repealed right after the war. They lied.

Take the case of the native Americans in southeastern U.S. who had their land confiscated by the federal government during WWII. These Americans were promised that the land was taken for wartime use only, and would be returned as soon as the war was over. To this day the land has never been returned to its rightful owners. The government lied, as usual.

Take the case of Bill Benson. He checked, in person, the archives of every State in the nation, plus the national archives, and discovered that the 16th Amendment never passed. It's the law that never existed. It's an illegal amendment to our Constitution. As a result, Benson did not pay taxes. He was arrested, brought to court, and his attorneys were made to submit more than 80 briefs, one after the other, in an obvious attempt to draw out the case. The judge made Benson perform his archival researches again, this time using procedures ordered by the court. Benson did so again, adhering to those procedures precisely. The results came out the same. So he proved under court ordered procedures that the tax law, the 16th Amendment to the Constitution, never passed, and is illegally being enforced. Our government lied again.

Nevertheless, the court found him guilty, and sentenced Benson to prison. He was on a medicinal schedule with a life-preserving medicine; the prison changed that and reduced him to practically a vegetable.

Our federal government is now starting to pass into existence laws equivalent to the Roman Catholic-State laws of the seven centuries of the Inquisition concerning property confiscation, both real and personal; also arrest, accusation, trial and conviction.

Our legislative and executive branches have passed a law that makes the arrest of property legal! Innocent persons are being arrested without a warrant, their property arrested also without a warrant, without evidence or proof of guilt. Their bank accounts, homes, cars, personal property arrested. How does a house, or a bank account, or a car, or a doll or bicycle or tricycle defend itself? How on earth does the victim defend himself with all of his estate confiscated? If he proves himself innocent, unbelievably, he is "allowed" to buy back his property. WITH WHAT? No bank account, property, cash, credit, or business? Will someone please convince me that our government has not deteriorated? Even if they repeal or modify this law, they passed it to start with. What next?

The sovereignty of our nation is vanishing. A citizen of another country can walk the streets of our country and arrest anyone he hears saying anything that he doesn't like.

President Lincoln predicted that our nation would die from action within, not from external attack.

How right he was! Now we are being made to pay for the criminality our government allowed for years by S&L and bank officers, executives and owners -amounting to billions upon billions of dollars.

All they can think to do is to raise taxes when they could accomplish more by cleaning up our government's house, by making our government Constitutional, by adopting into action the recommendations of the Grace Commission and the Hoover Commission, and by passing the Liberty Amendment. It's impossible to expect the legislators and executives to change their course to that extent. They are too far down the trail leaning on the destructive habits they are used to.

The Constitution specifically states that Congress has the power and authority to coin money and regulate the value thereof. Nowhere in the Constitution is the right to delegate that authority and responsibility granted under any circumstances whatsoever. Congress unconstitutionally delegated that authority and responsibility to a private bank, and it is costing our nation its economic lifeblood in interest.

There is terrible conflict of interest here; that bank wants the national debt to increase; it earns them more interest.

Deterioration of our government is achieved by the people in it approaching a cataclysm, bringing down their nation, just like the mice in the extremely low-density magnetic field environment experiment.

In the mice experiment, we see universal forcible rape around the clock and cannibalism as the ultimate signs of criminality during a low-density magnetic field environment.

In humans, we can see different refinements of that degree of criminality. Remember, those without empathy turn criminal first. Greed is the most common denominator contributing to criminal behavior. Rape and beating and murder follow closely. Behind all of the billions of the financial institutions' debacle is the greed of those causing the disaster.

Common to all criminal disaster is the criminals' mental state that they will get away with their crimes, that "No one will ever know". That is common to just about every criminal's mind. When those in power in the financial world are touched with this thought combined with their lack of empathy, they have entered into the world of crime. They might as well stand alongside the rapists, beaters, thieves and robbers, murderers, and be counted. They're all non-empathetic, leveling criminally with the lowering magnetic field density of our planet as it approaches the next cataclysm.

This is not an apology for their criminality. It's a damnation of welcoming one's self into an adulthood of no empathy - and the consequences are explicit. We are all responsible for our own acts, our own empathy.

This page is for the icing on the cake. The Constitution of the United States of America states bluntly: "Article IV, Section. 4.:

The United States shall guarantee to every State in this Union a Republican form of Government. and shall protect each of them against Invasions and on Application of the Legislature, or of the Executive (when the Legislature cannot be convened) against domestic violence."

The only process through which this guarantee, made in the supreme law of our nation, can be kepi is through the United States Government: I he President and the Legislature. Note that the italicized provision does not specify armed invasion; it includes any and all kinds of invasions.

The states of our nation have been invaded by some six million illegal immigrants- plus three million more this year. Total taxpayer costs: $35 billion.

Why has our government not honored its responsibility Constitutionally assigned to it?

Why are U. S. citizens losing their country to illegal aliens? Abraham Lincoln said it in 1838:

"If (U.S.A.'s) destruction be our lot, we must be ourselves its author and finisher. As a nation of freemen, we must live through all time, or die by suicide."

JESUS and CATACLYSMS

Now we come to the subject of Jesus and cataclysms. Matthew and Mark are the only places in the Bible where Jesus is quoted as discussing the subject. First, let's look at Matthew 24:35 thru 39.

"Heaven and earth shall pass away, but my words shall not pass away.

But of that day and hour knoweth no man, no, not the angels of heaven, but my Father only.

But as the days of Noah were, so shall also the coming of the Son of man be.

For as in the days until the flood came, and took them all away; so shall also the coming of the Son of man be."

Jesus follows this with examples and parables, exhorting His listeners to be prepared for the next flood. In 24:42 He says: "Watch therefore: for ye know not what hour Lord doth come."

The parables include the famous one about the ten virgins, five wise and five foolish; He again was exhorting His listeners be prepared. How many times has this scripture been read to us from a pulpit with no reference to Jesus' warning of a forthcoming inundation or cataclysm?

Mark offers a different version of the same discourse Jesus gave to one of His disciples. Here are some excerpts:

13:14

"But when ye shall see the abomination of desolation, spoken by Daniel the prophet, standing where it ought not, (let him that readeth understand,) then let them that be in Judaea flee to the mountains:

13:17 - 18

But woe to them that are with child, and to them that give suck in those days! And pray ye that your flight be not in the winter.

13:24

But in those days, after that tribulation, the sun shall be darkened, and the moon shall not give her light,

13:25

And the stars of heaven shall fall, and the powers that are in heaven shall be shaken.

13:26

And then shall he send his angels, and shall gather together his elect from the four winds, from the uttermost part of the earth to the uttermost part of heaven."

AFTERTHOUGHTS

I've been debating with myself for many years about two items to include in your survival equipment. These items are not necessary for survival, but are of a distinct, great advantage for post-survival knowledge. If you do survive, how do you know where you are? Where has the shell of the Earth's crazy rotation taken you? Or shall we say deposited you? And if you lay claim to any land, how do you record it? That means how do you record it accurately?

First of all, take a course in navigation. Purchase for yourself the book, Nathaniel Bowditch's Tables. Also, buy yourself the best Sextant you can find. Take care of it as if it were your life's treasure. Learn how to use it - become an expert. It can tell you your location. Learn your constellations of the stars - they will not change; only their location will. Take a sun dial with you. If you can, take a globe with you, and I/16" or 1/8" wide colored tape. You will be able to tape on your new equator.

For tools, take long and short levels.

Take a good stopwatch with you. Your day may be longer or shorter than 24 hours.

Take a course in surveying, and become an expert or have someone with you take this responsibility.

Purchase the best transit, tripod, surveyor's rod and surveyor's steel tape. If you want to record any property you may want to claim, you'll need them. Now, if you can't do it, at least do Paragraphs 2 and 3.

POSTLUDE

This is about a legend. I have struggled all through the writing of this shortest of pieces as to where to put it, and I finally was forced into this location for lack of a better place for it.

This is not "a" legend. I have found this legend countless times, which puts some aura of authenticity to it. Since it came from many widely separated places, if it did happen, it's more than a supreme coincidence that it did happen in so many places over the world concurrently. If it's a conspiracy to create so many identical legends, it would have taken an incredible, comprehensive and titanic effort to formulate it all over the world, and have not one person give away the fraud.

The legend is this: At the beginning of a cataclysm, or maybe just minutes or hours before the start, a plethora of space vehicles descends and picks up those whom they can so that they may survive.

The legends describe the scramble to board the survivors-to-be and the many space vehicles landing at each location. Only survivors not taken could relate it.

If it happens to you, be prepared for their ability to communicate with you so that you hear them in your head before they land. Answer; and always be sure to think precisely the words you say, for it is your thoughts that they receive. May the Great Designer be with you.

AFTEREFFECTS

Now is just about the right time to review the aftereffects of a cataclysm. It's difficult to imagine, but it's so, it's so - there are constructive byproducts of every cataclysm.

In past cataclysms - or perhaps due to only one cataclysm - some species have been eliminated which had hampered the growth of civilization and progress by the human race; a good example is the dinosaurs.

Our civilization, since the last cataclysm - known as Noah's, or Utnapishtim's flood - grew steadily at a reasonable rate until just a few centuries ago, when it started an upward turn in reproduction rate which is now rampant, uncontrolled, and with no concern for any responsibilities or consequences whatsoever.

During the time of reasonable growth, appalling and unchallenged authority was vested in religions and witchdoctory. If we look at one statistic alone, the Inquisition, which lasted over seven centuries, there were over three million humans executed in the warped name of Christianity, most by burning alive at the stake. Ninety-eight percent of those murdered by the church were women!

Appalling authority exists today on a stupendous scale in slavery, prostitution, female-selling, law, judiciary, medicine, banking, government, plus an astounding authority in being a criminal, a rapist, just a husband in many countries, religions, narcotics trade strong enough to defeat the IRS - plus including any government - and more.

We are witnessing an assault on our planet on a scale incomparable to any other time in known history. Pollutants dumped into the ocean arc destroying the oceanographic ecology worldwide. Pollutants dumped into the atmosphere from burning organic matter are destroying our air purity worldwide. Pollutants dumped into rivers are destroying those rivers, but further destroying the oceans into which the rivers flow. Rain forests of the world are being destroyed and burned at a rate which is staggering. Timber forests are being harvested and destroyed at an unprecedented rate.

Take Cape Cod, Massachusetts, for instance. It is a unique, modern civilization in today's modern U.S.A, in that it has no water supply system other than ground water. Wells are the only source of water; and further, the only sewage system available is septic tanks. City governments on the Cape have allowed developers and builders to build and develop, build and develop, - bringing more pollutants - until the ability of the ground to give pure water and take in sewage is not far from its ultimate doom.

And financial pollution? It took World War II to end our 1930's depression; will it take the next cataclysm to terminate our government's financial debauchery?

Greed has so invaded civilization that it has caused severe degradation of both the government and the finance industry - and so degraded industry that disregard of both laws and common sense is practiced concerning the infusion of terrible pollutants into and onto our planet - practiced in the interest of profit.

Natural resources are being depleted to where ends of supplies in nature can be foreseen.

Behavioral, moral, social and religious standards are deteriorating at a rate never seen before in written history. Terrorism is now a tool of church and state. The only comparable period is the seven centuries of the Inquisition, when that period of deterioration was through degradation of religious authority.

A cataclysm accomplishes many things: it stops unbridled and irresponsible reproduction, being the best population regulator known; it reshuffles all of the earth's natural resources; it stops the worldwide pollution of our planet, and provides for the restoration of pure water in lakes, rivers and oceans; it provides for the restoration of forests and rain forests the world over; and stops man's process of dehumanizing himself with narcotics, mass crime, and terrible authority. It provides time for restoration of ocean and freshwater life, plus restoration of a pure atmosphere.

And, above all, it gives mankind a chance to start over once more -and this time do it right - without intellectual or spiritual imprisonments.

Recommended Reading

The Bible All Versions

The Bible as History - Werner Kelle

Sex and Family in the Bible - Raphael Pata

Mysteries of Ancient South America - Harold T. Wilkin:

Secret Cities of Old South America - Harold T. Wilkin;

Gods, Graves and Scholars - C. W. Ceram

How Old is the Earth? - Patrick M. Hurley

The Calendar of Tiahuanaco - H. S. Bellamy & P. Allan

The Great Idol of Tiahuanaco - H. S. Bellamy & P. Allan Tiahuanacu, the Cradle of

Arthur Posnanski - American Man

Letters on the Physical History - J. Andre DeLuc

Of the Earth, Essay on the Theory of the Earth - Baron Georges Cuvier

Nine Planets -Alan E. Nourse

Design of the Universe - Fritz Kahn

The New Astronomy - A Scientific American Book

Primitive Man and His Ways - Kaj Birket-Smith

If you think we should not be concerned, take some time to think on this:

The United States Geological Survey and independent research Physicists have issued the statement that the Earth's magnetic field strength is decreasing at an accelerating-rate.